SEEK & FIND
CONTENTS

PICTURE HUNT 4

Suitcase	5
Yum	7
Maze	9
Stamps	11
Bugs	13
Street	15
Toys	17
House	19
Music	21
Photoboard	23
Red	25
Gallery	27
Picture Hunt Challenge	29

AMAZING 30

Flight	31
Space	33
Food	35
Tools	37
Arena	39
Nature	41
Blue	43
Numbers	45
Purse	47
Games	49
Monitors	51
Bedroom	53
Amazing Challenge	55

balloon

wind-up mouse

rocking horse

thimble

abacus

jack

wagon wheel

SPECTACULAR 56

Animals	57
Blocks	59
Spectacles	61
Green	63
Underwater	65
Pipes	67
Sport	69
Jigsaw	71
Circus	73
Bouquet	75
Gravity	77
Fireworks	79
Spectacular Challenge	81

MAGICAL 82

Imagine	83
Magic	85
Rainbow	87
Wish	89
Audience	91
Stage	93
Castle	95
Laboratory	97
Myths	99
Emporium	101
Halloween	103
Christmas	105
Magical Challenge	107
Seek & Find Challenge	108
Travel Games	109
Answers	110

Excalibur   Pan   griffin   voodoo doll   anvil   chameleon   Penny Farthing

PICTURE HUNT

SEEK & FIND

Collected things from many lands,
Are stored within a suitcase.
Can you spot two clowns, a coin,
A sad and happy face,

Two ducks, two dogs, two horses,
Two ways of telling time,
Three locks, five eggs, a pumpkin head,
And a red stop sign?

cowboy

ball

sun

statue (figurine)

train

shuttlecock

spoon

discus thrower

buffalo

Can you spot an egg of green, a white marshmallow, a gum-ball machine,
Two strawberries, a red candy bear, two ice cream cones, a creamy eclair?
Find two sweet hearts, a car, a muffin, four bananas, and three tiny buttons.

chocolate

fudge

sweet

chocolate egg

chocolate

swirl

chocolate truffle

biscuit

roll

8

Can you spot a clown
And a pear,
Four jacks, a thimble,
And a bear in a chair?

Can you find a
Tomato face,
A horse's head in
A silly place?

There's a rocket ship,
An owl in a tree,
And a way to get
From A to B.

telephone

a die

teddy bear

chair

shield

window

fire hydrant

flowers

duck

Can you spot five paper clips,
And a Chinese boat,
A rhinoceros, an elephant,
And a mountain goat?

Find the stamp from Musicland,
And a human brain,
A camel and a croissant,
A jet and two biplanes.

binoculars

biplane

boar

croissant

owl

rocket

Santa

shells

tweezers

Can you spot a cotton reel,
A nib, a tag, and a plug,
A yacht, a die, a bolt, a key,
And a bright red ladybug?

Can you find three house flies,
A needle, and a caterpillar,
Two centipedes, two spiders,
A hook, a nail, and a gorilla?

beetle

coin

red ant

hook

nib

paper clip

needle

praying mantis

snail

ROOM TO LET

P

Can you spot three arrows,
A window full of clocks,
A tiny little goldfish,
And an old mailbox?

Can you find five lemons,
A camera, and a cat,
A copy of this page,
And a baseball bat?

Can you spot a ship
And a hungry giraffe,
A sign that says FOR SALE,
Three candles in the dark?

1716

TELEPHONE

DR. MORSE'S
Indian Root Pills

GORDON'S
PIANOS.

LITTER

sign

camera

bag

seagull

skateboard

trash can

sign

astronaut

jug

16

Can you spot a wooden plane,
A piano, and a house,
A tractor, trike, and windmill,
A little wind-up mouse?

Can you find three horses,
A carrot in a truck,
A tambourine, a sewing machine,
And a fluffy yellow duck?

toy plane

trike

spaceship

panpipes

bird

panda

dolphin

clock

gypsy

18

Can you spot a pair
Of scissors,
A wagon wheel, and
A shiny mirror,

A pyramid and
A clock,
A dinosaur,
A hose, a sock?

There's a happy ghost,
An old-fashioned hat,
A pair of boots,
And a dancing cat.

badge

butterfly

tomato face

Aladdin's lamp

bolt

lamp

Viking helmet

watering can

shell

Find a saxophone, a gramophone,
A xylophone, a flute,
Four guitars, three tiny stars,
A golden harp, and a lute.

Music makes the world go round,
Seven trumpets can be found,
There's a clarinet, a ukulele too,
They all make wonderful, musical sounds.

musical note

castanets

cello

harmonica

lute

old radio

tambourine

gong

ukulele

The Bank of Smiles

To: Mother Hubbard
Address: The Shoe
           Nursery Land

01/01/2000

Account balance:
1/12/1999   Deposit   12 laughs
                 Deposit   17 hugs
                 Deposit   34 smiles
                 Withdrawal   9 tears

The more you invest in life, the more you get back from it.

A smile costs nothing, but can mean so much.

23

Note

Can you spot a spider,
A medal, and a boat,
A telephone, a turtle,
And a little love note?

Can you find a bicycle,
A violin, and feather,
A map, three green tacks,
And five kittens all together?

bracelet

dart

knight

paper clip

pencil

scissors

smiley face

sun

elephant

24

ribbon

bicycle

ice skates

balloon

lobster

fire hydrant

thumbtack

guitar

Can you spot
A bus and a train,
A monkey wrench,
And a jet plane?

Six strawberries,
Find them all,
A pair of lips,
And a ping-pong ball.

Can you find
A big toolbox,
A Christmas hat, and
Two Christmas socks?

bauble

Can you spot a fisherman,
A peacock, and a cat,
A racing horse, a picnic,
A dartboard, and a rat?

Can you find the television,
A tower, and a gnome,
A little yellow window
And HOME SWEET HOME?

Can you spot a vintage car,
A rabbit, and a dog,
A cow, a leaping dolphin,
And a little green frog?

camera

polar bear

fish

graveyard

mask

mountain goat

paint palette

THE END

HOME
SWEET
HOME

spider

3

windsurfer

squid

scraper

PICTURE HUNT
SEEK & FIND
CHALLENGE

boomerang

lizard

The following items are much harder to find, so get ready for the challenge!

CASE (pages 5/6)
2 owls
A musical note
A lizard
2 knights in armor
The Thinker
A viking ship

YUM (pages 7/8)
A bite
5 bears in a row
2 red twists
The word "HONEY"
2 lollipops
9 balloons

MAZE (pages 9/10)
A rainbow
4 barrels
The words "SPOT THIS"
The words "SPOT THAT"
A man with binoculars
3 horned helmets

STAMPS (pages 11/12)
2 leopards
2 stamps from nowhere
A stamp worth 4 peanuts
3 kings
A tiger
A lion

BUGS (pages 13/14)
Butterfly A
Butterfly B
Butterfly C
A knight in armor
A pig
4 clown faces

STREET (pages 15/16)
3 shoes
6 ducks
A lantern
A scary smile
A bonsai garden
A mirror

TOYS (pages 17/18)
2 dinosaurs
An eggbeater
Hammer & wrench
A lion
A purse
The cow that jumped
  over the moon

HOUSE (pages 19/20)
7 keys
A fire engine
A skull
A radio
3 chess pieces
A sailing ship

MUSIC (pages 21/22)
A banjo
An accordian
A pair of maracas
A bell
A tin whistle
Bongo drums

PHOTOBOARD (pages 23/24)
9 brass tacks
The words "HAPPY
  BIRTHDAY"
Tic-Tac-Toe
A piano player
A butterfly
A helicopter

RED (pages 25/26)
A tractor
Boltcutters
A hard hat
A feather
A clamp
2 boxing gloves

GALLERY (pages 27/28)
2 carousel horses
A gold teapot
A fork
A wrench
The letters "OFLCTB"
The words "THE END"

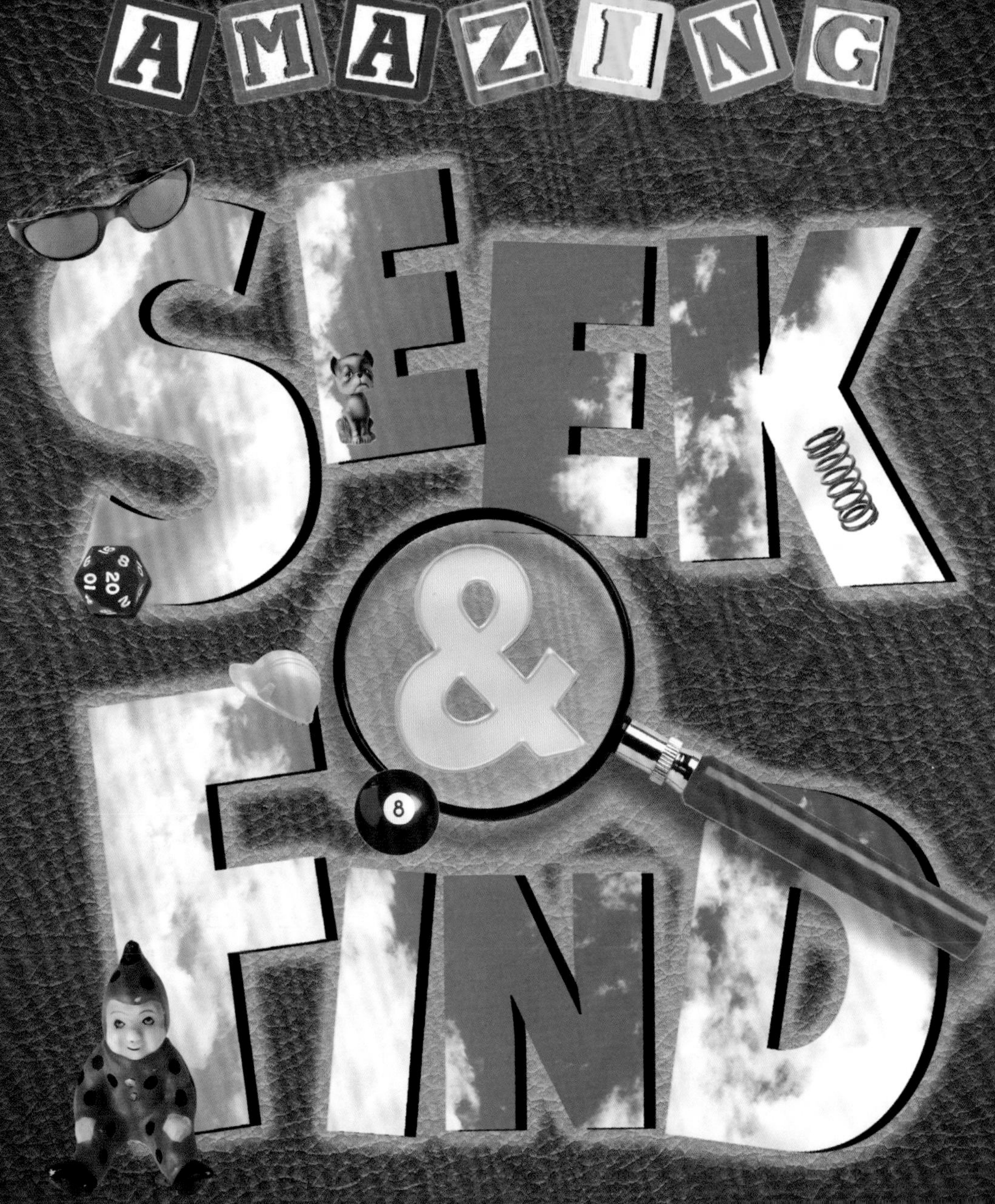
AMAZING
SEEK
&
FIND

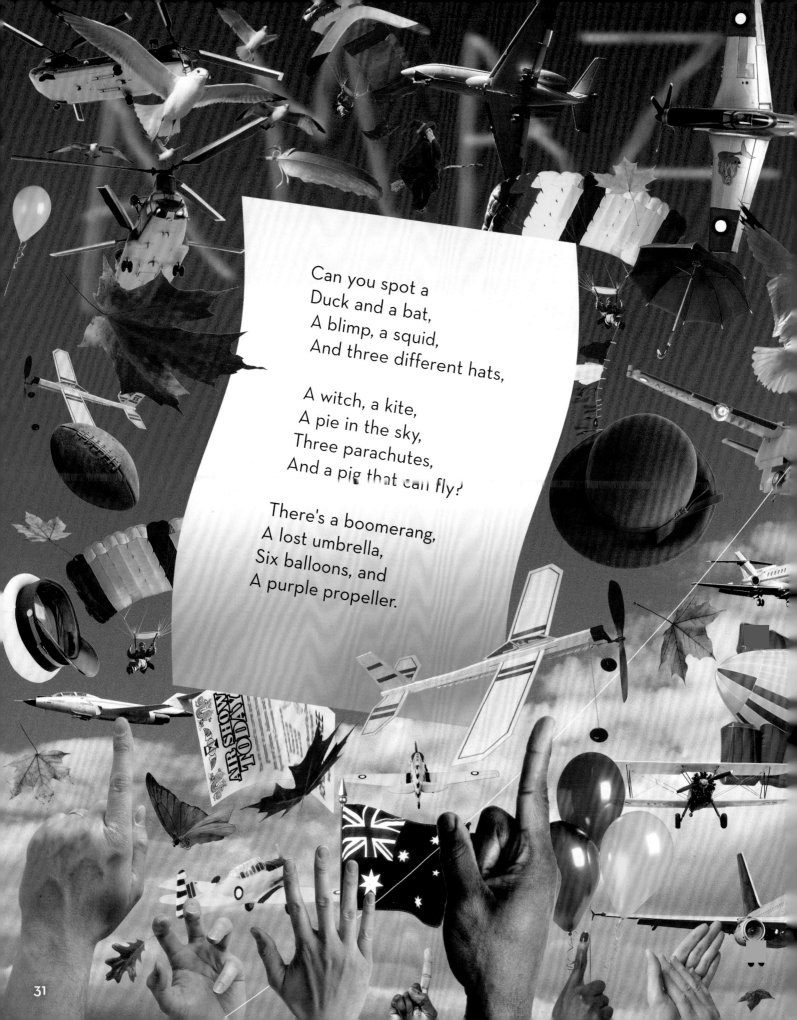

Can you spot a
Duck and a bat,
A blimp, a squid,
And three different hats,

A witch, a kite,
A pie in the sky,
Three parachutes,
And a pig that can fly?

There's a boomerang,
A lost umbrella,
Six balloons, and
A purple propeller.

plane

jet

pie

hand

witch

parrot

football

shuttlecock

blimp

32

Can you spot a magnet, a CD, and TV,
A sailing ship, a house, and a chimpanzee,
A barrel, a bottle, and four starfish,
Five astronauts and a satellite dish?
Find a golf ball, and a horse with wings,
A nut, a bolt, and planetary rings.

rubber duck

alien

bottle

badge

red lantern

star

skull

jack

badge

Can you spot an apple core,
A bunch of grapes, a soda can,
Corn on the cob, and two hot dogs,
A carrot, and a gingerbread man?

Can you find a pizza pie,
Three different types of cheese,
An avocado, half a tomato,
And four little honey bees?

almonds

avocado

broccoli

chick

ice cream

pasta

pear

radish

soda can

Can you spot a pair of pliers,
An ax, a vice, three colored wires,
A hard hat, and some plans on paper,
A dripping tap and a scraping scraper?
Find a torch, two springs, and two locks,
Three paint splats and a red toolbox.

vice

plug

brush

chisel

bolt

hammer

box of nails

plane

bolt

38

Can you spot a leopard,
A cow, two bulls, two seals,
Two stone cats, a welcome mat,
And three ferris wheels?

Can you find a baby bear,
A vintage car, a spear,
Five dinosaurs, a clock, a score,
A moose, a sheep, a deer?

knight

balloon

pawn

vintage car

clock

yo-yo

doll

ball

statue

40

AMAZING FALLS ->

Can you spot a kangaroo,
Five daisies, and a snake,
A soccer ball, a pineapple,
A hose, a spade, a rake?

Can you find a squirrel,
A shuttlecock, a gnome,
Three fairies, a canary,
And five pine cones?

flower

butterfly

sunflower

canary

orange flower

frog

hibiscus

hose

rose

Can you spot a bird and a pen,
A telephone, and ten past ten,
A truck, a puppet, two buckets, a tie,
A rabbit, a boot, and a butterfly?
Find a jukebox, a feather, a star,
A whistle, a flipper, a drum, and guitar.

bottle

kittens

clip

present

mouse

vase

paintbrush

stapler

vase

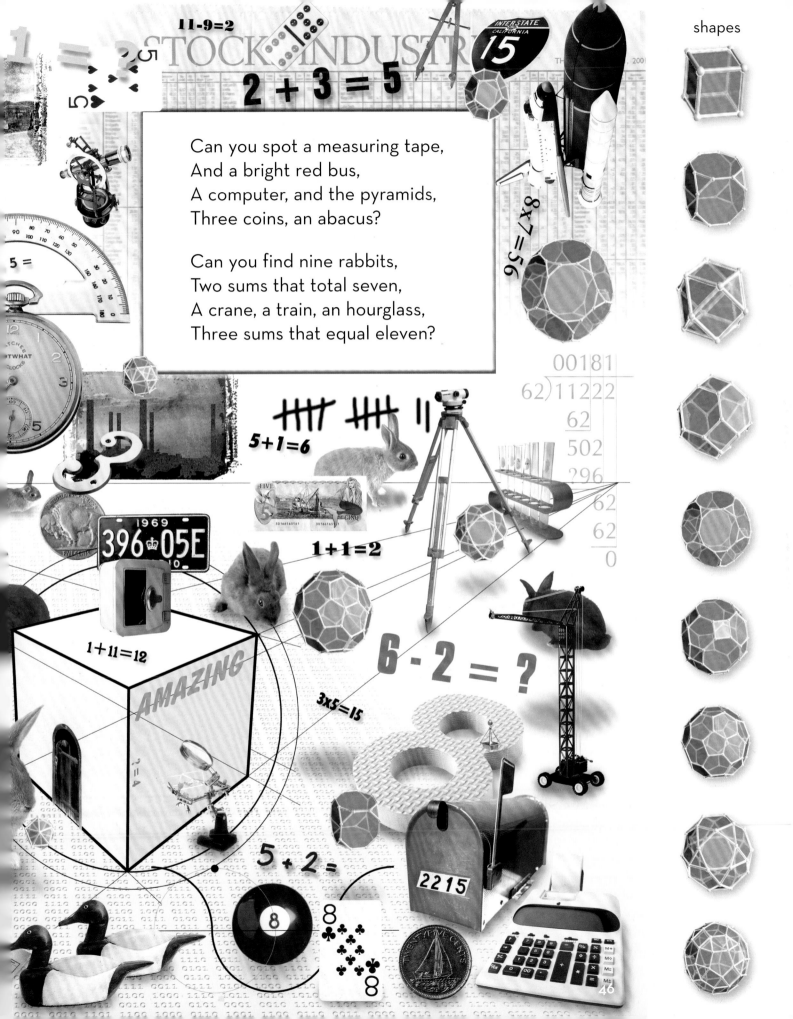

Can you spot a measuring tape,
And a bright red bus,
A computer, and the pyramids,
Three coins, an abacus?

Can you find nine rabbits,
Two sums that total seven,
A crane, a train, an hourglass,
Three sums that equal eleven?

Can you spot a set of keys,
And a red lipstick,
Seven coins, a pack of gum,
And a little candlestick?

Can you spot three brushes,
And a sticky first-aid strip,
Golden wings, five shiny rings,
And a tiny pair of lips?

thread

peg

button

brooch

button

pocketknife

thimble

nail clippers

tweezers

Can you spot three dominoes,
Two giraffes, and tic-tac-toe,
Three red dice, another blue,
A pawn, a knight, and a joker too?
Find eight jacks, a queen, a king,
Two darts, a clown, and a yo-yo string.

red ant

Scrabble™ piece

ten of hearts

coin

game piece

lighthouse

coin

gorilla

cannon

Can you spot a goldfish,
An apple, and cartoon,
A skier, wolf, and tomahawk,
A spider, and baboon?

Find a bear, a skunk, a poodle,
And a slide trombone,
A donkey and a lobster,
A watch and microphone.

bungee jumper

doctor

raccoon

remote control

splash

tomahawk

treadmill

trombone

world peace

Can you spot a pumpkin head,
Three balls, and a dragon,
Two lizards and a wizard,
And a little red wagon?

Can you find a pair of gloves,
Two orange boots, and a frog,
A car, a train, a cowboy,
Three mice, two cats, four dogs?

POEM
OF THE DAY

Fancy that,
A dancing cat,
To entertain the fans,

His only friend,
A singing hen,
Would clap if she had hands.

Benton Frappke December, 1908

54

duck

alarm clock

pogo stick

block

game pieces

gnome

cat

gorilla

moon

solitaire game

nib

Chinese boat

metronome

The following items are much harder to find, so get ready for the challenge!

FLIGHT (pages 31/32)
A butterfly
4 green leaves
3 hourglasses
An eagle
The world's first plane
A pair of socks
2 elastic bands

SPACE (pages 33/34)
All 12 zodiac symbols
A parking meter
A picnic
A space shuttle
4 telescopes
Venus and Mars
A kazoo

FOOD (pages 35/36)
3 balloons
3 chilli peppers
Some teeth
A Christmas tree
6 airborne peanuts
6 blue candles
6 strawberries

TOOLS (pages 37/38)
5 keys
A needle
3 cogs
3 measuring tools
3 different saws
A microscope
A metronome

ARENA (pages 39/40)
7 jacks
5 barrels
An Indian brave
A moon
4 shields
The words "GO GO DANCE"
A path to spell "AMAZING"

NATURE (pages 41/42)
A spider
An owl
A hungry bee
A nest
2 lizards
7 snails
A hummingbird

BLUE (pages 43/44)
A typewriter
A seahorse
12 musical notes
4 fish and 3 dolphins
4 boats
4 balls
A rocking chair

NUMBERS (pages 45/46)
The word "FEBRUARY"
2 boats
3 dominoes
A barometer
4 playing cards
The word "RADAR"
The sun

PURSE (pages 47/48)
5 diamonds
A frog
A cat
A pair of scissors
An umbrella
A ticket to Wonderland
A pen

GAMES (pages 49/50)
A fish bowl
A dog
4 flies
A thimble
Solitaire game
A pig
14 marbles

MONITORS (pages 51/52)
7 escaped butterflies
A potted plant
A rock band
A door handle
A jack
2 cameras
Headphones

BEDROOM (pages 53/54)
4 dinosaurs
23 yellow stars
An elephant
6 musical instruments
A fairy
A green plane
7 bears

Spectacular

SEEK & FIND

Can you spot two elephants,
Three giraffes, and a bat,
A lion, a tiger, a leopard,
An owl, and a pussycat?

Can you find four eagles,
Three dogs, a hippo, a moose,
A sheep, a mouse, and a rabbit,
A golden egg, and a goose?

SPECTACULAR GORGE

chicken

golden egg

guinea pig

kangaroo

macaw

peacock

polar bears

skunk

turtle

Can you spot a rocking horse,
A piggy-bank, a lollipop,
A sewing machine, a tambourine,
A submarine, a spinning top?

Find a helicopter,
A scarecrow and a bee,
A jack, a train, a crown, a plane,
And the letters 'ABC'.

cat

camera

bird

frypan

owl

crown

doll

plant

umbrella

Can you spot a birthday cake,
A telephone, a ring,
A rattle, and a thimble,
A ladybug, a wing?

Can you find a lobster,
An eyeball, and a key,
A skier and an ice cube,
A log, a nest, a tree?

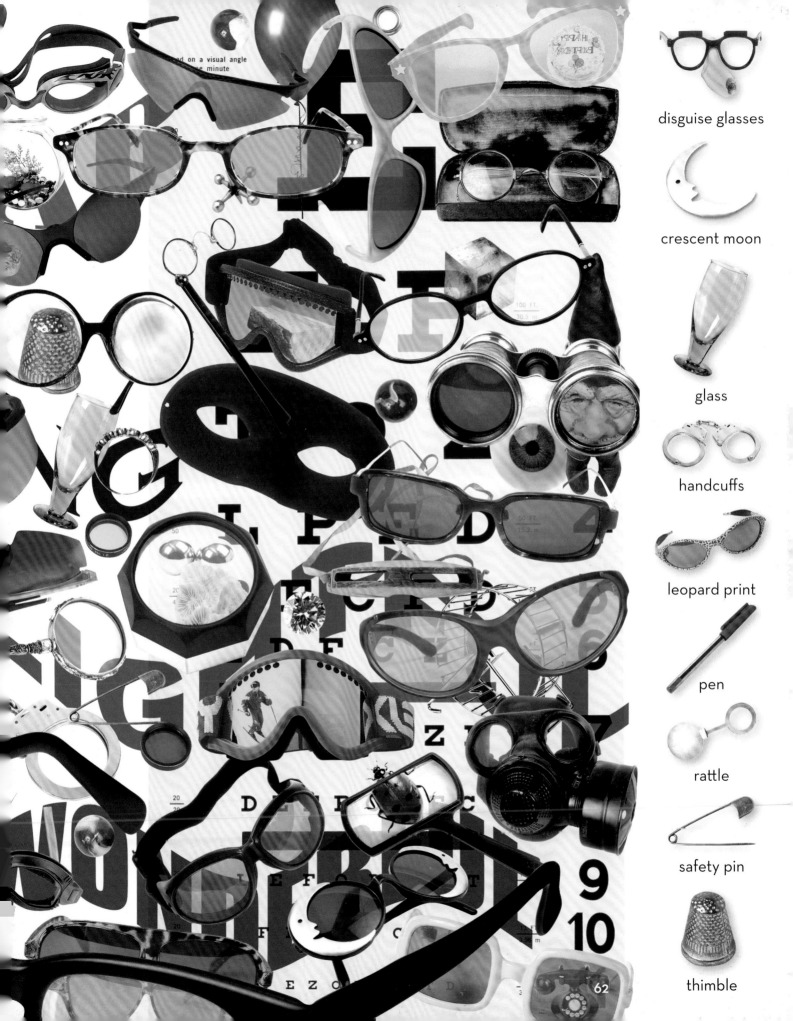

disguise glasses

crescent moon

glass

handcuffs

leopard print

pen

rattle

safety pin

thimble

Can you spot a watering can,
A Christmas tree, and a parrot,
A house, a lettuce, an olive,
A chameleon, and a carrot?

Find two snakes and a tractor,
A horn and six crawling insects,
Three frogs, a four-leafed clover,
And a Tyrannosaurus rex.

barrel

bauble

traffic light

bird

candy cane

cotton reel

zucchini

glove

chameleon

Can you spot a jellyfish,
A seahorse, and two skulls,
A turtle and a lighthouse,
One pearl and two seagulls?

Find five leaping dolphins,
A crab, a pair of oars,
An octopus, a treasure chest,
A coin, a kettle, a door.

65

fish

life jacket

ship

can

windsurfer

bell

gauge

shark

pirate flag

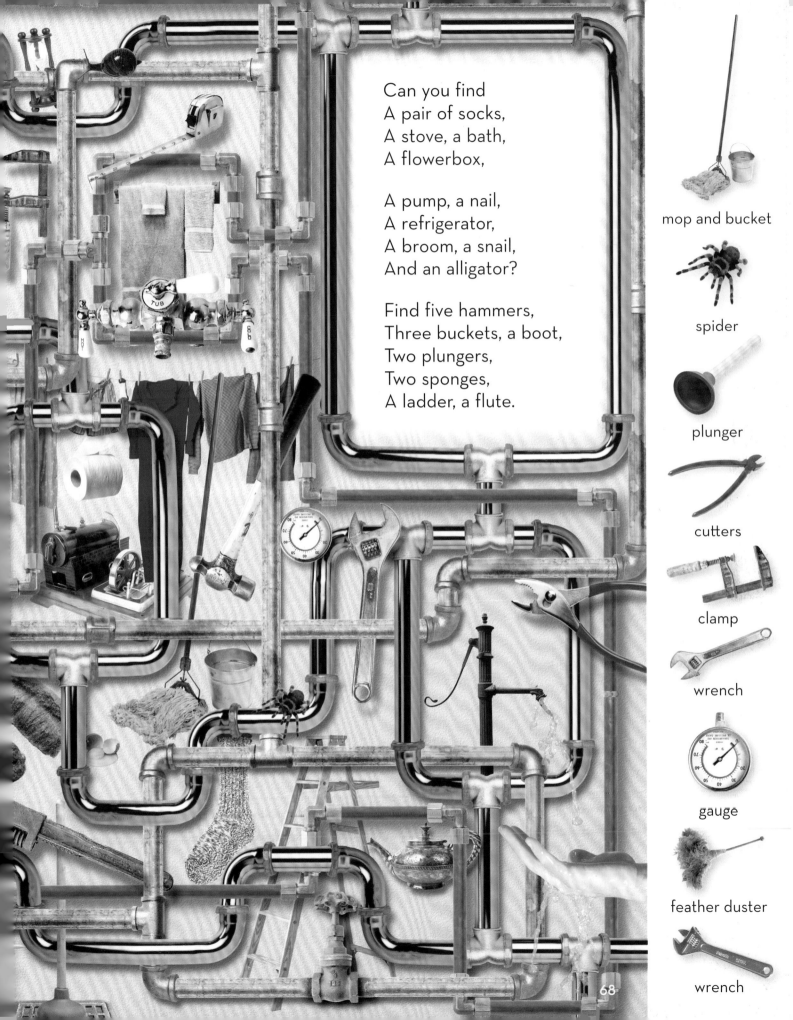

Can you find
A pair of socks,
A stove, a bath,
A flowerbox,

A pump, a nail,
A refrigerator,
A broom, a snail,
And an alligator?

Find five hammers,
Three buckets, a boot,
Two plungers,
Two sponges,
A ladder, a flute.

mop and bucket

spider

plunger

cutters

clamp

wrench

gauge

feather duster

wrench

SPOT WHAT

SPORTING SPECTACULAR

ADMIT ONE
0596033
0596033

Can you spot a basketball,
A tennis ball, two bats,
A jump rope, a bowling ball,
A fisherman's hat?

Find a pair of ice skates,
Two whistles, and a dart,
A stopwatch, a checkered flag,
A saddle, a horse and cart.

grip exerciser

boxing glove

rollerskates

discus thrower

ball

ticket

cap

baseball

weights

Can you find a scorpion,
A lizard, and a truck,
A surfboard, a skateboard,
A blackboard, and a duck?

Can you spot a windmill,
An astronaut, a car,
An eggshell, a footprint,
A statue, a guitar?

DINGELING BROS. CIRCUS

Roll Up! Roll Up!,
A spectacular to see,
The circus is in town,
Entertainment guaranteed!

Witness the high-flying
Fellini Brothers,
Perform death-defying,
Stupefying stunts above us,

With jugglers juggling,
Clowns clowning around,
The high wire dare-devils,
Dare-devillings astound,

A better time cannot
Be found anywhere,
So come on down,
To the Circus & Fair

KINDLY CONTROL YOURSELF

Frank Flemming's
Fantastic
Flea Circus

Can you spot a juggler,
Five stars, and seven clowns,
A trapeze artist, a unicyclist,
A chimp, and a merry-go-round,

A pair of tightrope walkers,
Three tumbling acrobats,
An apple, a pear, a balancing chair,
Three hoops, and a very tall hat?

cap

bat

pirate hat

bowler hat

hat

fez

mask

crown

teeth

To the Fellini Brothers,

Can you spot a ball of wool,
A stapler, and a fan,
A wagon wheel, a fishing reel,
An egg, and frying pan?

Find a candelabra,
A knife, a fork, and a pie,
A banjo and a compass,
An umbrella and bow tie.

Spectacular Flower Arrangments

SpotWhat?

angel

beaded maraca

candelabra

cup and saucer

dice

dolphins

pram

pincushion

wagon wheel

76

Can you spot a wishing well,
A parachute, a polar bear,
A bird in a cage, an open page,
A witch, and a rocking chair?

Find a worm and a cuckoo clock,
A brush, a comb, and a cello,
Two balloons, a shovel, a spoon,
And five little flowers of yellow.

apple

feather

light bulb

little red wagon

fan

bell

ball

seagull

telescope

Can you spot a jack-in-the-box,
A peacock, and a dragon,
A pirate and a rooster,
A ship, a mermaid, a wagon?

Find a hummingbird, a harp,
A unicorn, a kite,
A bucking bronco, a grand piano,
The name of a day, and a knight.

bucking bronco

mouse and cup

train

rose

Pegasus

flying pig

dog

rooster

swan

sundial

joker

SPECTACULAR SEEK & FIND CHALLENGE

candelabra

tuning fork

The following items are much harder to find, so get ready for the challenge!

ANIMALS (pages 57/58)
A frog
3 wise monkeys
3 lizards
2 feathers
Early bird gets worm
A spider and a fly
A snail

UNDERWATER (pages 65/66)
A catfish and a dogfish
4 starfish
4 scuba divers
A seal
2 anchors
A message in a bottle
7 seashells

CIRCUS (pages 73/74)
2 photographers
3 noisemakers
6 umbrellas
Comedy and Tragedy
2 elephants
A snake
2 elegant penguins

BLOCKS (pages 59/60)
9 balloons
A horn
A kettle
5 chess pieces
A piano
A coin
A star

PIPES (pages 67/68)
A teapot
5 toilet rolls
An egg
A coat hanger
A fire hydrant
A toilet brush
A set of plans

BOUQUET (pages 75/76)
A ship's wheel
An elephant
A gramophone
A fluffy bunny
A pair of ballet shoes
A guitar
A swan

SPECTACLES (pages 61/62)
A diamond
A rhinoceros
A light bulb
A fish bowl
9 marbles
A mirror
A jack

SPORT (pages 69/70)
A yo-yo
A hockey puck
5 soccer balls
A boomerang
2 catcher's mitts
2 shuttlecocks
2 pairs of binoculars

GRAVITY (pages 77/78)
A kitten
A dragonfly
The Mona Lisa
Time flies
East and west
The alphabet
A butter churn

GREEN (pages 63/64)
A circuit board
A leprechaun
Sunglasses
A brussel sprout
A watermelon
A window
10 green bottles

JIGSAW (pages 71/72)
10 gold bars
A wind-up mouse
A pair of scissors
A jet plane
A London bus
Chinese checkers
A match

FIREWORKS (pages 79/80)
The Pied Piper
A fish
A bow and arrow
A bridge
A fairy
A skipping girl
A court jester

Can you spot
A candlestick,
An alarm clock,
And a lion,
A frog, a snail,
A puppy dog's tail,
A soldier,
And an iron?

Can you find five
Rubber ducks,
Three mice, and a
Gingerbread man,
Three silver bells,
Four cockle shells,
A moon, and a
Watering can?

clock

cow and moon

plane

crayon

block

submarine

fish

marker

pinwheel

Can you spot a bowler hat,
An eggbeater, a toaster,
Two chickens, and a cherry,
A piano, a roller-coaster?

Can you find a bicycle,
A pencil, and a flipper,
Two bubbles and a joker,
A windmill and a zipper?

fishing hook

American money

UFO

torch

pawn

die

bow tie

sunglasses

bowler hat

Can you spot three radios,
A paintbrush, and a spring,
An icicle, five vehicles,
A kite, a reel of string?

Can you find a ping-pong ball,
Five flowers, and a lock,
A ladybug, three butterflies,
A cactus, and a clock?

balloon

flipper

leaf

light bulb

onion

drawing pin

house

wrench

teddy bear

88

Can you spot a candy cane,
A pair of pointy shoes,
A heart of gold, a peacock,
An egg, and three emus?

Can you find the planet earth,
A clover, and two fours,
A car, a boat, a train, a plane,
A sleigh, and Santa Claus?

ace of hearts

diamond

ribbon

tea cup
and saucer

present

tickets

four-leaf clover

shooting star

roses

90

Can you spot a cowboy,
A doctor, and a nurse,
Six robots, two teapots,
A parrot, and a purse?

Can you find a snowflake,
Someone fast asleep,
A hen, a fox, a jack-in-the-box,
And three of Bo Peep's sheep?

Santa

rubber duck

soft toy

frog

doll

balloon

dog

doll

teddy bear

Can you spot Napoleon,
A lollipop, a flute,
A camera, and a daisy,
A yo-yo and squashed fruit?

Can you find a saxophone,
A telephone, two crowns,
A tambourine, a flying machine,
A watch, a wand, three clowns?

FOR ONE NIGHT ONLY

lettuce

Napoleon

toy gun

baseball

rabbit

butterfly

eagle

horn

usher

94

Can you spot a rhinoceros,
A sheepdog, and a shepherd,
A big bad wolf, three little pigs,
A spinning wheel, a leopard?

Can you find three elephants,
A camel, and a llama,
A dodo, a stork, an old pitchfork,
Three goats, and an iguana?

cleaner

cow

leprechaun

deer

toy soldiers

curtsy

dodo

monk

pumpkin

Can you spot an onion,
A horseshoe, and a spoon,
A quill and four chess pieces,
A harp and a bassoon?

Can you find three seashells,
A dogfish, and a brain,
A fan, a mortar and pestle,
A lamp, and a candle flame?

The Almanac of Handy Hexes

bassoon

coffee grinder

knob

mortar
and pestle

hieroglyphs

brain

pterodactyl

mouse

witch

Can you spot a centaur,
Three skulls, a golden horn,
A scorpion, two griffins,
A witch, a leprechaun?

Find the Loch Ness Monster,
Three unicorns, a key,
A telescope, the pipes of Pan,
A fish, a dove, and a bee.

fountain of youth

book

compass

griffin

frog

sundial

dove

pipes of Pan

UFO

mushroom

Can you spot a gargoyle,
Three mirrors, and a moose,
A gnome, a coin, a violin,
A shuttlecock, a goose?

Can you find an hourglass,
Two swords, and a troll,
A pixie and a pyramid,
A boat and a voodoo doll?

flying carpet

stone crow

dreamcatcher

helmet

bird

sack of beans

sign

time flies

gargoyle

Can you spot a wagon wheel,
A rooster, and a crow,
A pirate and three apples,
Two ghosts, and a wheelbarrow?

Can you find the invisible man,
Two sacks, an ax, a skunk,
A hearse, a horse, a haunted house,
Three witches' hats, and a trunk?

candle

clown

hearse

ice cream

elephant head

toilet roll

doctor

vampire

vulture

Can you spot two reindeer,
Two penguins, and a bear,
A letterbox, three pine cones,
A fireplace, and a chair?

Can you find a snowman,
A puppy, and four cars,
A sailboat and a dinosaur,
Two tops and two guitars?

dice

flamingo

golf clubs

gramophone

ice sculpture

lighthouse

motorbike

piano

top

gargoyle

Napoleon

MAGICAL SEEK & FIND CHALLENGE

flying machine

obelisk

The following items are much harder to find, so get ready for the challenge!

IMAGINE (pages 83/84)
A heart
6 paper planes
An apple
A golden egg
An abacus
Fl 130
A family

MAGIC (pages 85/86)
A domino
A boomerang
A canoe
A nut and bolt
A light bulb
2 keys
An eye spying

RAINBOW (pages 87/88)
A bee
5 telephones
2 snakes
A pair of gloves
2 drums
A funnel
2 pairs of scissors

WISH (pages 89/90)
A winning hand
A bride and groom
7 pots of gold
A pineapple
An arched window
2 Christmas trees
A rabbit

AUDIENCE (pages 91/92)
A snake
Sunglasses
A soccer ball
A volley ball
A football
A tennis ball
Knitting

STAGE (pages 93/94)
A set of keys
A puffin
A vase
A penny farthing
A torch
A pen
A banana peel

CASTLE (pages 95/96)
Rapunzel
3 kings
A rooster
A mousetrap
Quasimodo
A pocket watch
A pirate flag

LABORATORY (pages 97/98)
A centaur
The solar system
A chocolate frog
A goose
2 butterflies
A coffee mug
An umbrella

MYTHS (pages 99/100)
The sun
The tooth fairy
Excalibur
The magic harp
A woodpecker
An obelisk
A tall ship

EMPORIUM (pages 101/102)
A saw
A hammer
A pair of pliers
A clamp
2 axes
A dart
3 wands

HALLOWEEN (pages 103/104)
Headless horseman
2 candelabras
A cowardly lion
3 lanterns
2 pumpkin pies
An oilcan
9 skulls

CHRISTMAS (pages 105/106)
2 gingerbread men
3 snowflakes
5 sleds
A pogo stick
A woolly mitten
A birdhouse
Spectacles

SEEK & FIND CHALLENGE

Did you notice that some things appear more than once?
Can you find the words "SPOT WHAT" in every picture?

lobster

In **PICTURE HUNT** can you find:

A fairy and a three,
A matchstick, an apple,
And a honey bee?

discus thrower

pinwheel

In **AMAZING** can you find:

A mermaid and a four,
A ladybug, a light bulb,
And a little blue door?

UFO

grip exerciser

In **SPECTACULAR** can you find:

The number ten, a gnome,
A butterfly, an hourglass,
And an ice cream cone?

plane

curtsy

In **MAGICAL** can you find:

A crystal ball, a cat,
A knight, a dragon, a wizard,
An owl, and a black top hat?

DOWN WITH
PRINCE
CHARMING

monk

SEEK & FIND TRAVEL GAMES

CALL AND SPOT

1. The oldest player goes first.

2. He or she is "the caller" and the other player is "the spotter". The caller chooses a page from the book and picks an item for the spotter to find, saying, for example, "Can you spot a boomerang?"

3. The spotter must then try to find the item.

4. If the spotter can't find it, the caller gets 5 points and shows the spotter where it is and has another turn.

5. If the spotter can find the item, then he or she gets 5 points and now it's his or her turn to be the caller.

6. The first to reach 30 points wins but you could also set your own limit or simply play best out of three!

7. You can make the game more challenging by putting a time limit of one to three minutes on each search.

SPOT AND RHYME

1. The youngest player goes first.

2. He or she is "the spotter" and the other player is "the poet." The spotter finds six items for the poet to use in a poem.

3. The poet then creates a four-lined poem making sure the end of the 2nd line rhymes with the end of the 4th line. For example, "dog" rhymes with "frog" in this poem:

> Can you spot a vintage car,
> A rabbit, and a dog,
> A cow, a leaping dolphin,
> And a little green frog?

4. Once a poem is created, the poet switches roles with the spotter.

5. You can make the game more challenging by increasing or decreasing the number of items to use in a poem.

ice skates

dog

vintage car

knight

gramophone

old radio

dancing cat

ANSWERS

SEEK & FIND

SUITCASE (pages 5-6)

Blue circles indicate objects listed in the poem and on the right side of the page.
Pink circles indicate objects listed in the *Seek & Find* challenges.

Collected things from many lands,
Are stored within a suitcase.
Can you spot two clowns, a coin,
A sad and happy face,

Two ducks, two dogs, two horses,
Two ways of telling time,
Three locks, five eggs, a pumpkin head,
And a red stop sign?

YUM (pages 7-8)

Blem circles indicate objects listed in the poem and on the right side of the page.
Pink circles indicate objects listed in the Seek & Find challenges.

Can you spot an egg of green, a white marshmallow, a gum-ball machine,
Two strawberries, a red candy bear, two ice cream cones, a creamy eclair?
Find two sweet hearts, a car, a muffin, four bananas, and three tiny buttons.

ANSWERS: PICURE HUNT

MAZE (pages 9-10)

Blue circles indicate objects listed in the poem and on the right side of the page.
Pink circles indicate objects listed in the *Seek & Find* challenges.

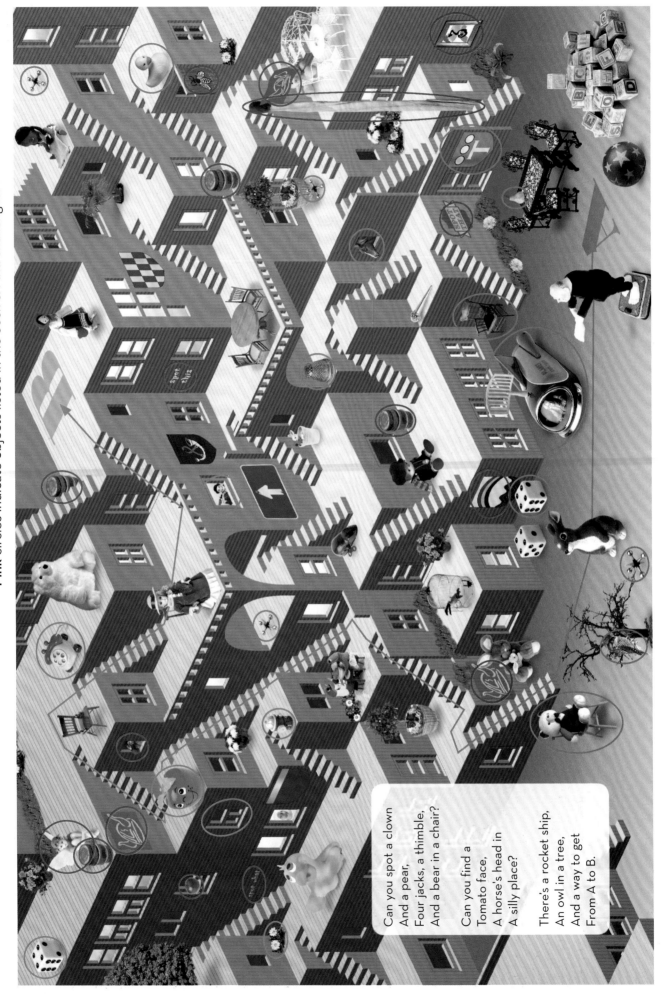

Can you spot a clown
And a pear,
Four jacks, a thimble,
And a bear in a chair?

Can you find a
Tomato face,
A horse's head in
A silly place?

There's a rocket ship,
An owl in a tree,
And a way to get
From A to B.

STAMPS (pages 11–12)

Blue circles indicate objects listed in the poem and on the right side of the page. Pink circles indicate objects listed in the *Seek & Find* challenges.

Can you spot five paper clips,
And a Chinese boat,
A rhinoceros, an elephant,
And a mountain goat?

Find the stamp from Musicland,
And a human brain,
A camel and a croissant,
A jet and two biplanes.

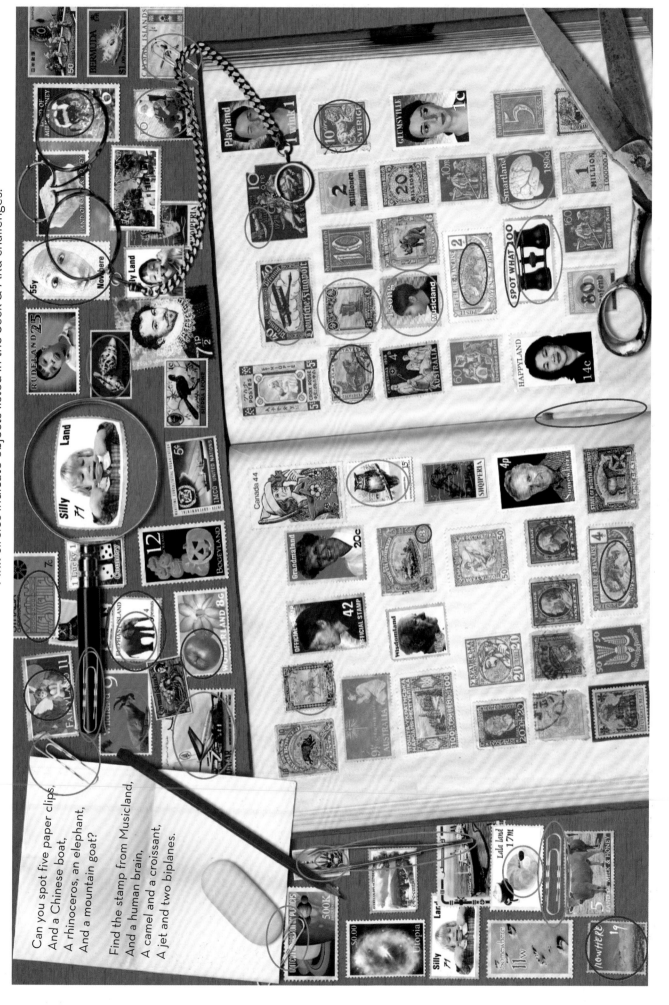

BUGS (pages 13–14)

Blue circles indicate objects listed in the poem and on the right side of the page.
Pink circles indicate objects listed in the Seek & Find challenges.

Can you spot a cotton reel,
A nib, a tag, and a plug,
A yacht, a die, a bolt, a key,
And a bright red ladybug?

Can you find three house flies,
A needle, and a caterpillar,
Two centipedes, two spiders,
A hook, a nail, and a gorilla?

STREET (pages 15–16)

Blue circles indicate objects listed in the poem and on the right side of the page.
Pink circles indicate objects listed in the *Seek & Find* challenges.

Can you spot three arrows,
A window full of clocks,
A tiny little goldfish,
And an old mailbox?

Can you find five lemons,
A camera, and a cat,
A copy of this page,
And a baseball bat?

Can you spot a ship
And a hungry giraffe,
A sign that says FOR SALE,
Three candles in the dark?

TOYS (pages 17–18)

Blue circles indicate objects listed in the poem and on the right side of the page.
Pink circles indicate objects listed in the *Seek & Find* challenges.

Can you spot a wooden plane,
A piano, and a house,
A tractor, trike, and windmill,
A little wind-up mouse?

Can you find three horses,
A carrot in a truck,
A tambourine, a sewing machine,
And a fluffy yellow duck?

129.   eBook Crossroads: Directory of ePublishers
Publishers
http://www.ebookcrossroads.com/epublishers.html

Aimed more at prospective writers, the site offers a "comprehensive listing of royalty paying, non-subsidy ePublishers complete with submission guidelines, formats and genre listings. The Directory is not an endorsement of the ePublishers listed, but an informational listing only." Publishers are listed alphabetically by name on two pages (A-L and M-Z), with a brief description – principally noting genres – and a link to the submission guidelines on their web site. Over 50 publishers are included.

130.   Every Writer's Resource: Ebook Publishers
Publishers
http://www.everywritersresource.com/ebookpublishers.
  html

Supported by 'Ads by Google', this is a simple list of about 60 e-book publishers with links to their web sites.

131.   Lida Quillen's ePublishers List
Publishers
http://www.sff.net/people/lida.Quillen/epub.html

The author of this page notes that it attempts "to mention only reputable, royalty paying, non-subsidy publishers [and] will not knowingly list a subsidy publisher." Some 43 publishers have been evaluated and are listed with genres, links to their web sites and their submission guidelines. A further 21 un-evaluated publishers, and 22 publishers now apparently out-of-business are also listed, as are a few additional resources and recommended readings. Newly added publishers are highlighted.

132.   FanFiction
Novels
http://www.fanfiction.net/book/

In some cases the writing here is more short story than novel, but it *is* fiction published without benefit of publisher and grouped by original inspiration – so there are some five titles grouped under 'One Flew Over the Cuckoo's Nest', seven at 'Fried Green Tomatoes at the Whistle Stop Cafe' and 186 grouped as 'Scarlet Pimpernel'. The web site itself is quite sophisticated and while initial access is by way of the lengthy list of group titles, within each of these it is possible to sort the list by date, or limit it by genre, rating (everyone to mature adult), language, length and status. Each title is listed with author, title, a very short summary and all the limit categories such as length or rating; most titles have linked reviews – although these may be no more than a line of affirmation – and authors are displayed as links which allow immediate access to all of their books.

Short stories appear as a single HTML page, but longer works are divided into chapters with a link to the next (or any other) chapter at the top and at the foot of the page beside a link to 'review this chapter'. At the top of each page there are also tools to vary the font, the font size and the font style, to move between full-, three-quarters- and half-width pages, to vary the line spacing, and to reverse the screen to print white on black.

133.   Smashwords
Various
http://www.smashwords.com/

Smashwords is an e-book publishing and distribution platform for authors, publishers and readers. It offers DRM-free e-books in a variety of formats for immediate sampling and purchase. There are no charges for publishing and distribution. Although Smashwords is not a major source for free e-books, it is included as it includes some free e-books and also allows readers to freely sample most works (in many cases, it is possible to read up to half of the book before committing to purchase). Most titles are priced below US$10.00. There is no indication of how many titles are available in total from the approximately 6,500 authors, but curiously the home page does report "*905,964,708 words published*".

The web site is more conventionally organised than FanFiction (*see*) with books listed under a variety of fiction categories as well as Biography, Business & Economics, Entertainment, Health and Well-being, Inspiration, Parenting, Poetry, Reference, Religion, and Self-improvement. Any of the fiction or non-fiction categories can be 'filtered' to list only the free e-books. The lists can also be filtered by books with fewer or greater than 25,000 words, or sorted by best sellers, most highly rated, most downloads and newest titles.

Titles are listed with details to the right of a small cover image, including title, author, price, length in words, a short abstract and – where it has been awarded – a star rating. Where there is also a conventional publisher details of where the complete book may be purchased are included (in several instances publishers had excerpted one short story from a collection and made it freely available through Smashwords).

Selecting a title from the list generates a screen with slightly greater publication detail, notes on parental rating and a list of subject tags. This is followed by a list of formats in which it may be either read online (HTML, Javascript, etc) or downloaded (Kindle, ePub, PDF, etc). Where there are more books by the same author(s), these are also listed.

134.   WattPad
Various
http://www.wattpad.com/

The About Us page states "Founded in 2006, Wattpad's vision is to revolutionize the way we publish and read written works. Wattpad is now the world's most popular ebook community where readers and writers discover, share and connect, delivering billions of pages from our library, one of the world's largest collection of originally-created ebooks. Wattpad provides a powerful creative outlet and social media for undiscovered and published writers to share what they have written - a romance story, fan fiction, poetry or novel - and attract millions of readers. All the written works are easily discovered on Wattpad's website, mobile site or through the Wattpad application available on all mobile devices including Apple iPhone/iPad, Android, BlackBerry, Nokia, Samsung and more."

From the Home page's featured works, it is possible to move to new or 'hot' titles, or to search by author, keyword or title. e-

Books which match the search are presented as a list with title, author, subject tags and a note on length (some are quite short, but many extend to book-length), the number of times the book has been read, and links to comments and ratings. Selected titles are presented as a series of pages (the middle two-thirds of the screen) with a voting button and ways of sharing (Facebook and Twitter) to the left. To the right is a note from the author giving an indication of reading age; a summary of the number of times the title has been read, comments and popularity, as well as the category; followed by some Ads by Google. The bottom of the page contains blog-like comments, and a link to the next section. The main text can have the font size varied.

SINGLE TITLES

135.   This Gaming Life: Travels in Three Cities
Monograph
http://quod.lib.umich.edu/cgi/t/text/text-
  idx?c=dcbooks;;idno=5682627.0001.001

This title by Jim Rossignol is an example of works published under the imprint of 'digitalculturebooks' (*see*) from the University of Michigan Press and the Scholarly Publishing Office of the University of Michigan Library, and is thus available for free online (under a Creative Commons Attribution-Noncommercial-No Derivative Works license) and for sale in print.

The book is a collection of essays looking at different aspects of the gaming experience. It is available only in HTML format, and does not seem to be available in any downloadable precompiled e-book format.

136.   Artcyclopedia
Encyclopedia
http://www.artcyclopedia.com/

The Artcyclopedia – "the ultimate guide to great art online" – covers   9,000 artists   and   2,900 art sites and   includes 160,000 links. Artists can be browsed by name, subject, nationality or medium and all the major art movements are also covered. Apart from the feature articles (e.g. "Venetian Rivals"), and the entries for movements (which are brief), artist records are composed of links both within the encyclopedia and pointing to sources for art posters, galleries, pictures within image archives, and auctioneer's sales. Factual information is limited to a brief biographical description or a quotation (in some cases), relationships with movements and other artists, and some images of works.

The encyclopedia can be searched by the name of the artist or work, and the location of works in museums and galleries. It also contains some 'slide shows' of related works.

137. Australian Dictionary of Biography (ADB)
Dictionary/Encyclopedia
http://www.adb.online.anu.edu.au/adbonline.htm

The work contains over 10,000 scholarly biographies of persons who were significant in Australian history prior to 1980, and may be browsed or searched by individual names, authors or occupations. The electronic version is equivalent to the printed *ADB*: Volumes 1 to 16 in the continuing series and the Supplementary Volume. Articles are said to be "concise, authoritative accounts of the lives of significant and representative persons in Australian history. It should be noted, however, that they were written progressively from the early 1960s to the present. Therefore, some may not reflect the latest scholarship or current mores. Print publication details, including the year, accompany each article... [T]he most eminent people in Australia's history are given articles of 2,000 to 6,000 words; other significant figures have entries that range in length from 500 to 2,000 words."

Browsing and searching are straightforward, and the advanced search screen offers a wide range of choices (e.g. gender, cultural heritage, religious influence) in order to focus the search. However arrived at, a list of possible names is offered with the possibility of ordering by name, birth or death years in either ascending of descending order. The final personal entry has a brief summary box containing alternative names, details of birth and death, religious influence and occupations. The full entry ends with a selective bibliography, the name of the author and a note of the print volume from which the entry was taken.

138. Chomsky: A Life of Dissent
Biography
http://cognet.mit.edu/library/books/chomsky/chomsky/

This is an electronic edition of Robert F Barsky's book, *Chomsky: A Life of Dissent,* which "explores the life and work of Noam Chomsky, investigating the political, philosophical and linguistic worlds within which we live, and about which Chomsky writes." It also offers a timeline and "an evolving range of dialogues and collaborative work on Chomsky's writings, and themes derived from his work."

The e-book is begins with a traditional contents page from which it can be seen that there are two sections: the Milieu that Formed Chomsky and the Milieu that Chomsky Helped to Create; these and individual chapters, as well as the conclusion, notes and a list of works consulted can all be accessed directly. Above this are buttons for 'Welcome', 'Credits', 'Contact' and 'Search'. Each section or chapter comprises one or more scrollable HTML pages with direct link at the foot to the following HTML page. In the left-hand margin is shown a list of equivalent pages in the print book, and external links to places, etc that are mentioned in the text. There are occasional images within the text.

The contents page can be revisited from the top of the page and there is a button linked to an order form for the print book at the foot of each page.

139. CIA World Fact Book
See also: **Library of Congress Country Studies**
Reference
https://www.cia.gov/library/publications/the-world-
   factbook/

The long-established US *CIA World Factbook* provides detailed information on the history, people, government, economy, geography, communications, transportation, military, and transnational issues for 266 world entities. It also includes regional maps and flags of the world. Before the web e-book became available it was published both in print and on CD-ROM. This e-book is now updated bi-weekly. Access is simply from the drop-down list of countries or directly to one of the appendices (for example, abbreviations, international organisations and groups, selected international environmental agreements).

Country pages begin with the flag, maps and in some cases photographs, and are then organised under a series of subheadings such as geography, people or economy – each with a brief descriptive overview followed by statistical data noting the year for which it was obtained. For each statistic there is a small icon that links to a comparative tabular display of the specific group of data for all 266 countries. From the Reference tab, it is possible to move to the 'Guide to Country Comparisons' which allows direct tabular comparison of specific fields such as life expectancy at birth or death rate. Pages can be printed; it is also possible to download the entire publication or to view a version designed for low bandwidth.

Users need to be aware that the search box which appears slightly above the drop-down list of countries relates to the parent CIA web site including the *Factbook*; this is also true of the left-hand menu, which includes, for example, 'Kid's Page'. Some data shows a distinct US bias such as the comparative size of the French-owned Clipperton Island in the Pacific Ocean which is given as "about 12 times the size of The Mall in Washington, DC"; although there is an entry for United States Pacific Island Wildlife Refuges, there is no entry for Palestine.

140.   City Sites
  Monograph
  http://artsweb.bham.ac.uk/citysites/

This inter- and multi-disciplinary study of the iconography, spatial forms and visual and literary cultures of New York and Chicago in the period 1870s to 1930s resulted from a research collaboration by scholars from Europe and the USA. It is a set of multimedia essays and exists only as a born-digital e-book published in 2000.

Because it began life digitally it was able to present "an entirely new conception of what an electronic book might look like", and was developed to take full advantage of the medium both in terms of the book structure and in the use of animations, sound, moving images and film clips to full advantage; it also allows readers to move away from linear reading, either by following internal links in the text or by pursuing one of several thematic paths (e.g. architecture) through the chapter texts. The developers says that "in keeping with the notion of a book format – it exists as a bounded and finished structure, within which users experience considerable freedom of movement but also extensive guidance and signposting to orient them within the book's complex structure". There is a long essay on the development and structure in the project overview, which is accessible from the contents.

141.   Cookbook
Reference
http://en.wikibooks.org/wiki/Cookbook:Table_of_
Contents

This is a cookery book developed in a wiki as a part of Wikibooks (*see*); as such it is a collaborative effort to document all aspects of cooking from recipes to culinary techniques to which anyone may add material. The contents page offers access to cooking techniques, basic food groups, special diets, ingredients, national and ethnic cuisines, nutrition and equipment as well as to recipes, which are divided into sub-categories such as beverages, salads or soups.

Many of the sections are quite detailed, and recipes all have ingredients list and a procedure; this may be preceded by a general description, pictures, a table of times, etc.

142.   Dictionary of Art Historians
Dictionary/Encyclopedia
http://www.dictionaryofarthistorians.org/

Duke University's dictionary describes itself as a "biographical and methodological database intended as a beginning point to learning the background of major art historians of western art history. A free, copyrighted scholarly database for the use of researchers, students and the public." It is a compilation of art historians mentioned in major art historiographies with some additional entries and acknowledges that it is a "work in progress" begun in 1986. It exists in German, French, Italian and Dutch in addition to English.

Access to individual biographies is by means of an alphabetic name list. Some entries are brief – limited to a sentence, while others extend to several paragraphs of text. All begin with the dates and places of birth and death, and end with a list of sources and in some cases a bibliography.

143. Encyclopedia of Life (EOL)
Encyclopedia
http://www.eol.org/

With a home page topped by a quotation from Edward O. Wilson: "Imagine an electronic page for each species of organism on Earth..." the Encyclopedia of Life is an "unprecedented global partnership between the scientific community and the general public". The goal is to make knowledge about all the world's organisms freely available. The site notes that "over the next five years, the EOL aims to generate a million species pages, most of which will be authenticated by experts; digitize a large portion of biodiversity literature; generate educational materials for students, schools and universities; and use the EOL resource to generate new synthetic knowledge about the world's biodiversity." By mid-2010 hundreds of thousand of species had been added (there are 1.9 million known species in the world).

As with wikis, readers can register as members and add text, images, videos, comments or tags to the EOL pages. Quality is guaranteed as expert curators authenticate core collection materials submitted by all projects (scientific experts, learned societies and institutions) and individual contributors.

There are an initial six or seven highlighted species on the home page and a search box which will search species (the primary listing), tags or full text and produces a list of hits from which to select. The 'item page' consists of images (with other tabs for maps and comments) with the hierarchical species classification to the right, enabling further exploration around the located subject. Beneath this are three columns: in the left-most there is a detailed table of contents, while the right-hand side offers the possibility of adding images or text, or seeing a list of the latest changes. In the wider central column is the text of the section selected from the table of contents. Text may come from Wikipedia, ARKive or from a range of other sources, but where it (or the images, maps, etc) have not been evaluated by EOL curators there is a yellow background to signify the lack of review. Most articles are detailed and in many cases may be structured as a complete entry from one source followed by a complete entry from a second source. The source of the material, with the rights holder, licensing information and a link to the original, is clearly indicated for each section of the text.

144.   Encyclopedia Smithsonian
Encyclopedia
http://www.si.edu/encyclopedia_si/

The encyclopedia comprises over 2 million records with images, video and sound files and ranges across art and design; history and culture; and science and technology. The front page offers access to all three as well as listing categories drawn from all three disciplines. While it may be encyclopedic in stature and nature, the work is dependant on the Smithsonian's collections, departments and museums so that it may be seen to have a US bias or be less than comprehensive; it is certainly true to say that each category or topic leads to disparate assemblages of resources rather than a conventional encyclopedia 'entry' – as such its inclusion here may be stretching the definition of e-book too far. For example 'Transportation History' (nicely linked from 'Cars' in the alphabetic list) includes links to the [Smithsonian] American History Museum Transportation Collections – a brief overview and selected items listed with photographs; to 'America on the Move' – "Journey though the history of the United States to learn how transportation changed American lives and landscapes"; to 'Ship Plans' – "The Smithsonian's collection of watercraft plans is a valuable resource for the maritime historian, the student of naval architecture, other scholars, the model builder, and craftspeople"; and to 'A Brief History of Lighthouses' which includes a collection of lighthouse postcards online; as well as much more. This is clearly an invaluable and wide-ranging collection of resources, but it is rare to find a written encyclopedic article.

145.   Founders Constitution
Scholarly
http://press-pubs.uchicago.edu/founders/

The University of Chicago Press site describes this book as "the *Oxford English Dictionary* of American constitutional history" and goes on to note that "the print edition of *The Founders' Constitution* has proved since its publication in 1986 to be an invaluable aid to all those seeking a deeper understanding of one of our nation's most important legal documents... In this unique anthology, Philip B. Kurland and Ralph Lerner draw on the writings of a wide array of people engaged in the problem of making popular government safe, steady, and accountable. The documents included range from the early seventeenth century to the 1830s, from the reflections of philosophers to popular pamphlets, from public debates in ratifying conventions to the private correspondence of the leading political actors of the day."

On the contents page, individual sections are divided into sub-sections which in turn link to pages of links to the texts, all of which are available as HTML files, as are indexes of short titles, documents, authors, cases, and constitutional provisions. Individual links to texts lead to the text of primary materials. There is also a search facility.

146. Grimm's Fairy Tales
Literature
http://www-2.cs.cmu.edu/~spok/grimmtmp/

This is a basic HTML book containing the 209 fairy tales collected by the brothers Grimm. Curiously, the introduction notes that the exact print source is unknown: "The etext appears to be based on the translation by Margaret Hunt called *Grimm's Household Tales*, but it is not identical to her edition. (Some of the translations are slightly different, the arrangement also differs, and the Grimm's scholarly notes are not included.)" The collection is offered in the original order with each tale on a separate page.

Tales are printed unadorned and with no illustrations or formatting.

147. How to see the World
Monograph
http://www.artoftravel.com/

The full title of this 2009 book by John Gregory is *How to see the World. Art of Travel; European and World Backpacking on $25 a Day or Less*. The author describes his work as "25 chapters, 100,000 words, and 120 illustrations ... Written by an independent traveler of 35 countries via eight economical tours, this complete online guide has tips, commentary, and humor for travelers of every kind. It contains no advertising or commercial contracts." The chapters include People and Diplomacy; Passports and Visas; Walking and Backpacking; Essential Items; Organization and Packing; and Poems.

Each chapter or section is a single scrollable HTML page with a grey world map background and a black font, interspersed with colour photographs to illustrate the text (e.g. images of different backpacks). Usefully, each chapter's browser title includes the number of pages and the number of illustrations. The text is wise, simple and straightforward advice.

148.   Little Brother
Novel
http://craphound.com/littlebrother/download/

Quotations from two reviewers on the site note "A worthy younger sibling to Orwell's *1984*, Cory Doctorow's *Little Brother* is lively, precocious, and most importantly, a little scary" and "I can talk about *Little Brother* in terms of its bravura political speculation or its brilliant uses of technology – each of which make this book a must-read – but, at the end of it all, I'm haunted by the universality of Marcus's rite-of-passage and struggle, an experience any teen today is going to grasp: the moment when you choose what your life will mean and how to achieve it." It is available for download in three formats: plain text, HTML or PDF under a Creative Commons Attribution-Noncommercial-ShareAlike license which allows sharing and 'remixing' and conversion to additional e-book formats providing this is on a non-commercial basis. Some such conversions (e.g. to ePub) by readers are also available from this page.

149.   Mathematics : Introduction to Real Analysis
Textbook
http://ramanujan.math.trinity.edu/wtrench/misc/index.
shtml

The site states that this is the 2003 (updated April 2010) book by William F. Trench, previously published by Pearson Education. The free e-book is made available as a PDF download "in the hope that it will be useful as a textbook or reference. Reproduction is permitted for any valid noncommercial educational, mathematical, or scientific purpose." A complete instructor's solution manual is available by e-mail, subject to verification of the requestor's faculty status.

150.   Mobile Learning: Transforming the Delivery of Education and Training
Monograph
http://www.aupress.ca/index.php/books/120155

An e-book version of this print title published in March 2009 by Athabasca University Press is available for downloading for noncommercial use under a Creative Commons licence. The editor, Mohamed Ally, is a Professor in the Centre for Distance Education, and describes his book as follows: "This collection is for anyone interested in the use of mobile technology for various distance learning applications. Readers will discover how to design learning materials for delivery on mobile technology and become familiar with the best practices of other educators, trainers, and researchers in the field, as well as the most recent initiatives in mobile learning research. Businesses and governments can learn how to deliver timely information to staff using mobile devices. Professors can use this book as a textbook for courses on distance education, mobile learning, and educational technology."

Either the entire book or individual sections and chapters are available for downloading as PDF files. A MARC record for the book is also available for downloading in '.mrc' format.

151.   New Georgia Encyclopedia
Encyclopedia
http://www.georgiaencyclopedia.org/nge/Home.jsp

The *New Georgia Encyclopedia* contains nearly 2,000 authoritative articles on the people, places, events, and institutions of Georgia, as well as more than 5,000 images, audio and video clips on the history, culture, and life of the state. There is also a 'Quick Facts' section – did you know Georgia has exactly 100 miles of coastline?

There is hierarchical subject access under Arts, Business & Industry, Cities and Counties, Education, Folklife, Government & Politics, History & Archaeology, Land and Resources, Literature, Media, Religion, Science & Medicine, Sports & Recreation, and Transportation, as well as browsable lists of articles and authors. There is also a search and advanced search capability.

Articles are often quite lengthy; where possible including illustrations and usually ending with suggested readings. The narrow right-hand column beside the text contains lists of related links, both within the encyclopedia or elsewhere.

152.   Reading About the World, Volume 1
Encyclopedia
http://www.wsu.edu:8080/~wldciv/world_civ_reader/worl
d_civ_reader_1/contents_vol_1.html

The 3rd edition of the print title, *Reading About the World, Volume 1* was published by Harcourt Brace Custom Publishing in 1999, and was edited by Paul Brians, Mary Gallwey, Douglas Hughes, Azfar Hussain, Richard Law, Michael Myers Michael Neville, Roger Schlesinger, Alice Spitzer, and Susan Swan. It includes "short selections sharply focused on major topics of interest to beginning students of World Civilizations. It combines traditional historical sources with literary and philosophical selections." The text can be sampled here on the Washington State University web site through a significant number of excerpts made available as discrete HTML pages.

153.   Spartacus: Encyclopedia of the First World War
Encyclopaedia / Textbooks
http://www.spartacus.schoolnet.co.uk/FWW.htm

Although difficult to navigate, this text-book-come-encyclopedia offers a wealth of information linked to excerpts from primary material. As a born-digital e-book, it does not expect users to read it linearly and this may account for the compilers choice of the terms encyclopedia in its title. The heavy use of advertising and links to relevant books on Amazon can be distracting but the extensive content rewards those who persevere! It is intended for use in schools.

Access is by way of a two-part table of contents. Firstly there are sections on Chronology; Outbreak of War; Allied Armed Forces; Central Powers; Important Battles; Technology; Political Leaders; British Home Front; Military Leaders; Trench War; The Soldiers; and Major Offensives. These are followed by a link to First World War Digital Archive, and a second table with links to War at Sea; War in the Air; War Artists; War Literature; War Heroes; Women at War; Organisations; Strategies & Tactics; Weapons & Machines; Inventors and the War; Theatres of War; and War Statistics. Many of these point to a second list of links and thus onwards to text pages.

The content is presented in HTML pages – some short and others more lengthy. All contain further links to other pages within the encyclopedia, and in some case there is primary material following the text. For example, following the entry on the British Expeditionary Force there are two journalists' description – one from the *Manchester Guardian* of 18th August, 1914. Following each entry are also some further potentially useful links, but care must be taken as not all are internal.

The Second World War, which follows a similar pattern, and further historical and other textbooks are also available from the home page of this site.

154.   Tennessee Encyclopedia of History and Culture
Encyclopedia
http://tennesseeencyclopedia.net/

The online edition of the *Tennessee Encyclopedia of History and Culture* is a comprehensive reference work on the 'Volunteer State' co-sponsored by the University of Tennessee Press and the Tennessee Historical Society and containing the 1,500 entries of the 1998 print edition.

There are image, media and map galleries and the main encyclopedia can be browsed by way of topical categories or searched (title, author or full text). Categories include Agriculture, Conservation, Events, People, Politics and Sport. The main index also offers the preface, foreword, a list of authors and an extended essay, 'This Land Called Tennessee'.

Articles vary in length from a single paragraph upwards, and may include suggested readings. Nearly all include 'see also' references but these are not hyperlinked and must be located separately. Slide shows of images relating to the article being viewed can be accessed from the foot of the left-hand master menu, which – like the browse alphabet across the top of the page – is always visible.

155.   Yale University School of Medicine Heart Book
Textbook
http://www.med.yale.edu/library/heartbk/

The 29 chapters of this 1992 title edited by Barry L. Zaret, MD, Marvin Moser, MD and Lawrence S. Cohen, MD can all be downloaded as PDF files from the contents page at which the site opens. The web site but not the e-book was last updated in 2002. The book – clearly intended for lay use – is divided into six parts: The heart and how it works; How to lower your risk of heart disease; Steps in making diagnosis; Major cardiovascular disorders; Special situations; and Methods of treatment. Also included is an encyclopedia of common heart disorders and appendices with a glossary, a directory of resources and a selected bibliography. The title page and index can also be downloaded as PDF files.

The Foreword notes: "This book should not be used to alter a regimen prescribed by your physician or to devise your own treatment program – this should be entrusted only to a physician who knows your medical history. Instead, the information in this book is intended to improve your role as an informed partner in maintaining or achieving cardiovascular health."

EXPERIMENTAL PUBLISHING

156.   217 Babel Street
Novel
http://217babel.com/

"An evolving web of stories" - is described as "a web of interconnected stories set in a seaside apartment block. There are twenty apartments in the building. Each of the four writers [Susanna Jones, Alison MacLeod, Jeff Noon and William Shaw] works independently of the others, starting off stories from different rooms. New pages are produced by creating a link from a word or a phrase on a page that already exists. Writers can interrupt and take over each other's stories, taking them in different directions. Month by month the narrative changes, expanding into new rooms, characters and situations, creating new pathways for readers to explore."

As a born-digital work of fiction, the novel was able to take full advantage of interactivity which affected both the way the work developed and the way in which it may be read – any reader is likely to follow a new path through the maze of 'rooms' and thus through the plot.

157.   DQ Books
Graphic novels
http://www.dqbooks.com/

This is a collection of four short artist- or graphic-books, although while the site is called 'DQ Books' the text uses the terms 'magazine' and 'issues' in noting that new releases will be infrequent. Some of the volumes contain sexually explicit images and one deals with drugs. They can be viewed in a series of double-page spreads to the accompaniment of music, using Adobe Flash to present the page images. The books/issues are: *Invasion* ("Seven days of graphic improvisation: Capitalist invasion and mixed techniques."); *Seasons* ("16 illustrators, artists and photographers invent the life of a woman according to seasons. Mixed techniques."); *Where is the party?* ("Brazillian, Italian and French artists for a narcotic party, carried out with blue Bic ™ pen"); and *Beneath a steel sky* ("From Brooklyn to Central Park beneath a steel sky. Analog photography by Festo").

The authors describe the collection as: "a variable geometry project born from a four hands graphic improvisation: Festo (1hOS.com) meets Telmolindo (telmolindo.com) in "Invasion". Artists, illustrators and photographers will join [joined] the team in the second issue ("Seasons") for a sixteen people collaboration. Interdisciplinary "cadoure exquis" game, artists involved follow the rules of imposed theme and technique in an impromptu narration. French composer Avril created the original soundscapes."

158.   Under the Table
       Short story
       http://www.theurbanelitist.com/short-storyspreadsheet-
       excel-as-a-trojan-horse-for-literature/1947/

David Nygren's Excel download of a novel – a 'novexcel' is available from this blog page which describes the background to the project. Essentially the spreadsheet contains the novel: "the first worksheet of the Excel file has the "raw data," the story itself (8 columns x 30 rows). The easiest way to read it is to click on the first cell and then use the arrow keys to move to the next cell you want to read. The second sheet has a line graph that gives graphical representation to the "Character Intensity of Thought Units" (CIT Units) for each "Action Segment" in the story."

159.   We Tell Stories
       Short stories
       http://www.wetellstories.co.uk/

This is Penguin's experiment with writing *for* the medium as opposed to *in* the medium by digitising print books. In it, they persuaded six authors to write six multimedia books making full use of Internet and media facilities. The authors – Charles Cumming, Toby Litt, Kevin Brooks, Nicci French, Matt Mason and Mohsin Hamid – took as their inspiration six classic titles to produce *The 21 Steps, Slice (The Haunted Doll's House), Fairy Tales, Your Place and Mine (Thérèse Raquin), Hard Times* and *The (Former) General in His Labyrinth (Tales from the 1001 Nights)*. Each is completely different from the others in style and in its use of the medium. In *The 21 Steps* Google Maps are used to track the plot across London; the story in *Splice* is developed by reading two blogs and – in a similar way – *Your Place and Mine* is told in two voices in two timed columns; *Fairy Tales* allows the reader to interact with the story; *Hard Times* is a surreal series of page images; and *The (Former) General* places the reader on the page as the main character who must navigate the text in different ways; for example from the first page it is possible to return to the instructions, reminisce about their childhood, leave their office, or listen Shaan Azad's tale.

This is a rare example of a publisher and authors working together to produce works that exploit, and are uniquely appropriate to, the medium through which they are intended to be read. Well worth a visit!

SOCIAL E-BOOKS

160.   A Million Penguins
Collaboratively authored novel
http://thepenguinblog.typepad.com/the_penguin_blog/20
07/03/a_million_pengu.html (Post mortem)

This was a joint venture between Penguin Books and De Montfort University to produce a social novel written in a wiki – a collaborative creative writing exercise. The project has now finished but while the novel was being written many threads of discussion on the wiki surrounded and – undoubtedly – influenced the work; some 1,500 readers commented on, and collaborated in, the growing story and other writers responded to these comments. These could be read on the wiki 'Discussion' tab until the site closed. Readers could move directly from a brief description, past a contents list to the first section; further sections were on different wiki pages.

As the Penguin Blog notes, "Nearly 1,500 individuals have contributed to the writing and editing of *A Million Penguins*, contributing over 11,000 edits making this, in the words of Penguin's Chief Executive, 'not the most read, but possibly the most written novel in history'." Despite imposing "reading windows" when the novel was 'frozen' so that the editors could catch up, the project became unwieldy and is said to have attracted cyber vandalism. This may be the reason that the book is no longer available.

161.   The Basement Interviews
Monograph
http://dspace.dial.pipex.com/town/parade/df04/The%20B asement%20Interviews.htm

The Basement Interviews is a blog-based free (or open access) e-book of interviews conducted by the journalist Richard Poynder with leaders and thinkers from the growing number of free and open access initiatives, such as Project Gutenberg (*see*) or the Open Source Initiative. Introductions to the interviews are published on Richard Poynder's Open and Shut blog (http://poynder.blogspot.com/), each interview linked from this home page. The full interviews are made available from the blog, as PDF files published under a Creative Commons licence.

The interviews took place during 2006 and 2007 and feature: Michael Hart, the founder of Project Gutenberg; Richard Stallman, founder of the Free Software Movement; Eric Raymond, co-founder of the Open Source Initiative; Jay Rosen, proponent of Open Source Journalism; Lawrence Lessig, leader of the Free Culture Movement; Cory Doctorow, cyber activist and specialist in copyright and digital rights management; Vitek Tracz, seminal open access publisher; Harold Varmus, Nobel laureate and co-founder of open access publisher Public Library of Science; Richard Jefferson, leading advocate for the Biological Open Source Movement; and Peter Suber, de facto leader of the Open Access Movement.

162.   Book Glutton
Various
http://www.bookglutton.com/

Book Glutton not only provides free access to a range of e-books, but offers a social reading experience too. Social reading can be described as reading and discussing the text as a group, and in the case of Book Glutton the group may be closed (defined by you and limited to friends, classmates or a seminar group) or open (anyone reading at the same time as you). Every page being read has two panes that can be opened to left and right: one allows annotation (either public or private) and the other offer a real-time conversation with fellow readers in a way that is not unlike Windows Messenger or Facebook conversations.

Initially BookGlutton offered a range of out-of-copyright texts but now they have added titles from McGraw-Hill, Spineless, Girlebooks, Hunter Publishing, The Disinformation Company, Random House, and – most recently – IT and computing books from O'Reilly. Many books remain freely available but some (typically those from the recognised publishers) now have a purchase charge before they can be read. The interface offers facsimile pages one-by-one centre-screen with the interactive panes on either side. Navigation is straightforward and there is an option to increase the font size.

163. Building iPhone Apps with HTML, CSS, and JavaScript
Monograph
http://ofps.oreilly.com/titles/9780596805784/

Subtitled "Making App Store Apps Without Objective-C or Cocoa", this 2009 book by Jonathan Stark was created using the Open Feedback Publishing System, and was or is an O'Reilly experiment to "bridge the gap between private manuscripts and public blogs". The system allows comments from readers as the book builds; each comment is linked at paragraph level to the draft text. Input was welcomed in the form of questions, comments, suggestions or corrections.

Now completed and published by O'Reilly, the complete text is available, chapter section by chapter section, on this site. Each paragraph has links to comments in the right-hand margin; clicking on these inserts them in a box in the text following the relevant paragraph. It is only possible to view a single set of paragraph comments at a time. It remains possible to add comments.

164. Citizendium

*See also: **Wikipedia***
Encyclopedia
http://en.citizendium.org/wiki/Main_Page

Citizendium is an online encyclopedia project that is currently in a beta testing stage, and is described as "a citizens' compendium of everything... an open wiki project dedicated to creating a free, comprehensive, and *reliable* repository of structured knowledge. Our community is built on the principles of trust and respect; contributors, or 'citizens', work under their own real names, and all are expected to behave professionally and responsibly. Additionally, experts are invited to play a gentle role in overseeing the structuring of knowledge." There is a charter which is supposed to shape the project and the behaviour of contributors.

To date, there are about 14,850 articles of which just over one thousand are fully developed and 148 are approved by experts. There are articles for the natural sciences, the arts, the humanities, the social sciences, recreation, and the applied arts and sciences, each divided into smaller subject workgroups looked after by an editor. Articles may be found by moving through the hierarchical subject structure; alternatively, there is a search facility with two buttons: 'Go to page' identifies the main entry for the search term while 'Search' identifies all articles containing the term. All articles are clearly identified as either external article (i.e. brought in from a source such as Wikipedia; a stub (sufficient to identify the topic but not yet written); developing and in the process of being written; developed and virtually complete; or approved. The project began as an offshoot from Wikipedia which allowed more stringent editorial control and peer review of the original entries; it now seems to have moved to a stage at which most articles are freshly written.

Articles are of normal encyclopaedia or wiki length and, as with most wiki pages, each has its own internal table of contents and may include images. Again following normal wiki practice, within the text there are links to related articles or to empty pages where it is felt that an article is needed to cover a topic – a stub.

165.   Flight Paths: A networked novel
Novel
http://www.netvibes.com/FlightPaths

Created and 'curated' by Kate Pullinger and Chris Joseph, Flight Paths "uses stories, texts, videos, photos, sounds, and animations to tell the story of Yacub, the man who fell from the sky, and Harriet, the woman who witnesses his fall. It's a tale of refugees and migrants, consumers and cities, the desperate journey of one man and the bored isolation of one woman." It is open to contributions from anyone and material can be e-mailed or uploaded via the blog on this Netvibes page. Gradually a multi-faceted story is being developed.

166.   Gamer Theory (or more accurately, **GAM3R 7H3ORY**)
Monograph
http://www.futureofthebook.org/gamertheory/

Together with the Institute for the Future of the Book, McKenzie Wark created this text as a way to think to about computer games, as he developed his next book, GAM3R 7H3ORY. As the book grew, the software developed by the Institute allowed readers to contribute to each paragraph with their comments. The book is now complete and has been published by Harvard University Press. Here, the complete book is available as chapters, each of which appears as series of index cards – five cards or paragraphs at a time – the comments visible to the right of each card-paragraph relating only to that piece of text. The forum for commenting is now closed.

167.   *The Golden Notebook* Project
Novel
http://thegoldennotebook.org/

Although not originally a social e-book, or even an e-book, Dorothy Lessing's famous book was converted to an e-book as a social reading project. During 6-8 weeks in 2008, seven women authors read and commented on the e-book as they read it. Although initially limited to seven other readers were invited to join the growing conversations – "Good conversations are messy, non-linear and complicated. The comment area, a chronological scrolling field just isn't robust enough to follow a conversation among an infinite number of participants. Seven may even be too many. [Note: the forums are open to everyone and we do hope that readers beyond the initial seven will join the fray there both as regards the text and the process. We really want to know what you think works and what doesn't." The project was a part of "a long-term effort to encourage and enable a culture of collaborative learning... [to] understand how to model a complex conversation in the web's two-dimensional environment".

Comments are at the page level and it does not seem to be possible to add new comments although further discussion is invited in the blog and forum. Each page has a header and footer showing the section, the page (online, UK edition and US edition) and a search the book box. Summaries of the comments made can be viewed beneath the textual part of the web page.

168. The Holy of Holies: On the Constituents of Emptiness
See also: **Without Gods: Towards a History of Disbelief**
Monograph
http://www.futureofthebook.org/mitchellstephens/holyofh
olies/

Michael Stephens is a Professor of Journalism at New York University and has combined with the Institute for the Future of the Book in a project which he describes as, "a conversation. I am presenting a collection of some of the more controversial ideas from the early chapters of my book [Without Gods (*see*)] on the history of disbelief. The ideas are organised loosely around a single theme: the Roman leader Pompey's forced entry into the most sacred place of the Jewish temple. At issue are the origins and prevalence of doubt, even at the heart of religion."

What has evolved is effectively a short e-book in its own right, with twelve chapters, each replete with comments and queries from readers.

169. Libertary: Freedom of the Book
Various
http://www.libertary.com/

Like BookGlutton (*see*) the Libertary collection provides a platform for social reading; unlike BookGlutton this is not currently done alongside the page being read but in separate discussion fora for each book. The home page offers a few featured titles and access to the collection through eight categories: Politics - History - Business - Law; Health - Science - Technology; Fiction - Poetry - Memoir; Self Help - Inspirational; Instructional - How To; Entertainment - Sports; Religion - Philosophy and Other; or by way of an author list, a title list, new titles, or searching for authors or titles.

From the brief listings (a Google-like title, author and abbreviated first sentence of an abstract), there is a link to a summary page with the full description, a cover Image and the chance to purchase the book. In the left-hand column is a chapter list leading to the full text of each chapter, a search facility for the full text of the book, and a link to the book's discussion forum.

Chapters are presented as single scrollable HTML pages with the print-copy pagination shown. The left-hand column remains so that access to other chapters is immediate, as is searching or links to the discussions.

170. *Mortal Ghost* and *Corvus*
See also: **L Lee Lowe Online Fiction**
Novels
http://lleelowe.com/

These two full length novels from L Lee Lowe were written chapter by chapter in a blog, in order to facilitate comments from his readers. The books are free to be read chapter by chapter online or downloaded as a PDF file (or chapter files) and, now they are completed, may also be purchased in hardcopy. Both are also available as weekly podcasts while *Mortal Ghost* is also available in audiobook format. Each chapter comprises a single long scrollable page. All the fiction available from this site carries a Creative Commons Attribution-Noncommercial-No Derivative Works License.

Both titles received reader accolades while they were being delivered via the blog, a new chapter each week. Both are tense, psychological thrillers.

171. **Planned Obsolescence**
Monograph
http://mediacommons.futureofthebook.org/mcpress/plann
edobsolescence/

Kathleen Fitzpatrick notes that the "text you are now reading, whether on a screen or in a printed version, began its gestation some years ago in a series of explorations into the notion of obsolescence, which culminated in my being asked to address the term as part of a workshop organized by the Committee on the Status of Graduate Students, entitled 'Keywords for a Digital Profession,' at the December 2007 Modern Language Association conference." *Planned Obsolescence: Publishing, Technology, and the Future of the Academy* is published by NYU Press. Copyright (c) 2009 New York University although the text of the e-book "may be distributed in part or in whole on condition that (1) distributed text is not sold, whether or not such sale is "for profit" and (2) distributed text bears [the copyright] notice in full."

The complete text with bibliography, prefaced by a 'how to read and comment' section and two external reviews is available as an e-book. During its development online, the text was created in a wider left-hand column while the software allowed readers and reviewers to comment on paragraphs, pages or the whole book in a narrower column to the right. The comments can still be viewed beside the text and it is still possible to add comments or responses to existing comments. The website is powered by Commentpress, an open source theme and plugin for the WordPress blogging engine that allows readers to comment paragraph by paragraph in the margins of a text.

172.   The Platform Book
Monograph
http://prosaix.com/pbos/book-6-0.html

Joseph J Esposito's 2006 short draft text is available as an e-book – a processed book project, which invites comments on the text from readers. The text is presented as a single page, with author's notes – which in some cases appear to be edited versions of reader's notes, accessible from the right-hand margin. Highlighting a section of text produces a drop-down menu offering the possibilities of creating a bookmark or a note; creating an 'outgoing' or 'incoming' link; or creating a 'Bizvantage' topic.

Esposito describes a platform book as "a dimension of an electronic book in a networked environment in which other books, notes, and commentary were built upon the original book, the platform." This text is an example.

173.   Temeraire Wiki: Victory of Eagles
Encyclopaedia
http://www.temeraire.org/wiki/Main_Page

This wiki presents an encyclopedia of the Temeraire novels by Naomi Novik: *His Majesty's Dragon; Throne of Jade; Black Powder War; Empire of Ivory; Victory of Eagles* and *Tongues of Serpents*. Each book has a page with a cover image and summaries of books the story in some detail, and concludes with short sections on characters, trivia, deviations from history and – where available – reviews. There are also separate pages covering dragons, military, people, places, timeline, artwork and images. There are some 446 pages all together.

174.   The Wealth of Networks
Monograph
http://www.benkler.org/wealth_of_networks/index.php?titl e=Main_Page

Yochai Benkler's book, *The Wealth of Networks: How Social Production Transforms Markets and Freedom*, originally published by Yale University Press in 2006 is now available under a Creative Commons Attribution Noncommercial Sharealike license from this wiki site. It is available in several formats including HTML (formatted in separate chapters and available from the Conference of Non-Governmental Organizations web site) and PDF. You can also read reviews, discussions, interviews and link to 'remixes' or projects which have used the Creative Commons freedom to develop alternative versions.

The author notes that "With the radical changes in information production that the Internet has introduced, we stand at an important moment of transition", and his multi-award-winning and thought-provoking book describes the "social production [which] is reshaping markets, while at the same time offering new opportunities to enhance individual freedom, cultural diversity, political discourse, and justice." *(Publisher's description)*.

175.   We Think
Monograph
http://www.wethinkthebook.net/book/home.aspx

Leadbetter writes that "We Think explores how the web is changing our world, creating a culture in which more people than ever can participate, share and collaborate, ideas and information." The first three chapters were available on the website at the time of writing in 2006, and they remain there now, as is the complete draft of the book which is now available from Amazon. The chapters and draft are available in PDF format.

176.   Wikipedia
See also: **Citizendium**
Encyclopedia
http://www.wikipedia.org/

The precursor to Citizendium, Wikipedia is perhaps the best known social e-book – an encyclopedia compiled by the masses for the masses! Anyone may join the community and create, edit or add to pages – the consequence of this is that it is almost certainly the largest and most comprehensive encyclopedia available. The shortcoming is that there is no guarantee that the information supplied is accurate or well-written. In reality inaccurate, poor or erroneous information is usually spotted and corrected very quickly, but there is no formal peer-review process as there is in Citizendium. Wikipedia is often condemned because there is no formal editorial process – no quality control – but, used sensibly, it is an unrivalled source of information written by experts.

It is available in several languages – the English version has over 3,432,000 articles in Arts, Biography, Geography, History, Mathematics, Science, Society, and Technology. Browsing through the subjects is hierarchical, later stages often including brief summaries, so leading readers deeper into the subject. There is also a search function which takes readers directly to the main entries.

Articles generally start with a brief summary followed by a detailed hierarchical table of contents showing all of the sections further down the page. Images are often included, and articles end with footnotes and references. Length varies, and many articles are quite long, single pages – although the use of sectional headings makes access quite easy. As with all wikis, the text is laced with links to other articles.

177.   Without Gods: Towards a History of Disbelief
         See also: **The Holy of Holies: On the Constituents of**
                  Emptiness
         Monograph
         http://www.futureofthebook.org/mitchellstephens/

Without Gods was the blog-based discussion which developed during 2006 as Michael Stephens's book grew; some of the earlier chapters formed The Holy of Holies (*see*) project, which is still extant. After a year of debate and writing, the author "withdrew to his study" to complete his project – the blog archive remains. While this is not an e-book, it remains a record of the development of one.

GATEWAYS

178.   The Assayer
         Various
         http://www.theassayer.org/

The Assayer is a gateway to a variety of free e-books – it claims to be the "web's largest catalog of books whose authors have made them available for free." It is not necessary to subscribe, but having done so (it is free and only requires an e-mail address) members can review – and respond to reviews of – books. Books can be browsed by subject, author, title or reviewer; in the title browse, only, it is possible to limit the search by the degree of copyright freedom. Books are categorised as "Copyrighted, with a licensing agreement that prohibits selling or permanent use (an anti-book)"; as "Copyrighted, with no licensing agreement (a traditional book)"; as "Copyrighted, doesn't cost money to read, but otherwise not free"; as "Public domain"; as "Copylefted, but with restrictions on modification and/or sale"; or as "Copylefted: anyone can read, modify and sell". Subject browsing is by way of twenty top-level categories, with titles then listed in sub-categories. Given the claims to size it is surprising that, with each of the twenty categories listed with its number of titles, these total only 1,308. The majority of books have no reviews; where there is a review present it is appended to the bibliographic record and may be of any length.

Clicking on a title produces a bibliographic record (title, author, date entered, copyright freedom, subject, review(s) and notify) with a link to the source. As with any gateway, it is impossible to specify the format of the books; nor can the links be guaranteed – during the review process both broken and hijacked links ("Account of a Voyage around the World / J Roberts, John Bear" led to a plausible URL selling vitamin D pills) were noted. A logged-in reader could have reported these by way of the 'notify' section of the bibliographic record.

179.   Books-On-Line
Fiction
http://67.118.51.201/bol/default.cfm

The home page (in grey, blues and yellows) notes that this is a "Directory of books that are posted on the net and available for downloading at no charge along with new books being published" – some 59,376 "*mostly* free" e-books. The site also offers to e-publish books for which they will then pay a royalty of 10%.

It is possible to access the e-books on the site by browsing by subject; by author/title or keyword searches; there are recommended titles for fiction, non-fiction and classics; and lists of the most popular books for all titles, new titles, biography, mystery, science fiction, civil war, fiction, history, and computers. The site also lists the ten most significant books of the second millennium, "along with thoughts on some also rans".

By whichever route you come to it, there is a page for each title containing a brief summary and (possibly) some queries by previous users, followed by a list of sources. Things are not always what they seem! Selecting the monthly fiction best seller Othello by William Shakespeare brings you to a page with three names beneath the title – William Shakespeare, Oliver Parker and William James Craig – a description which begins "Movie Script and Play – Movie Review", two almost unreadable queries, and a list of sources which includes HTML (Bartleby, *see*), three 'Buy from Amazon' (book, DVD, VHS), two 'Images' (Second and Fourth Quartos from University of Pennsylvania, broken links), and a text file of the movie script (also a broken link). There is also a means to report broken links.

180.   Community College Open Textbook Collaboration
Textbooks
http://www.collegeopentextbooks.org

The Community College Open Textbook Collaborative (CCOTC) is funded by The William and Flora Hewlett Foundation, and comprises "a collection of colleges, governmental agencies, educational nonprofits, and other education-related organizations. [It] provides training for instructors adopting open resources, peer reviews of open textbooks, an online professional network, support for authors opening their resources, and other services." CCOTC acts as an access point or gateway, locating and evaluating open textbooks. The e-books are not stored on the CCOTC web site but links are developed to the textbooks that are considered worthy.

The links can be browsed by the following subjects: Anthropology and Archaeology; Art; Biology; Business; Chemistry; Computer Science; Economics; Education; Engineering; English and Composition; Health; History; Languages and Communications; Literature; Math; Music; Philosophy; Physics; Political Science; Psychology; Science; Sociology; and Statistics and Probability. In each case titles are listed with those that have been peer-reviewed indicated by a red asterisk; if they are not recommended the initials 'NR' will follow the asterisk and the title will have a line rules through it. Some are also reviewed for accessibility. All reviews can be read online. In each case, the title is also followed by a set of unexplained initials in parenthesis: CC for Creative Commons; BY indicating the need to attribute the work; SA for Share Alike, meaning that if you alter the work and make the new work available it must be made available under an identical licence; and NC for non-commercial use only.

As this is a gateway, some identified titles may have been removed from their server while remaining visible on CCOTC.

CCOTC also contributes to MERLOT (*see*) and Connexions (*see*).

181.   Digital Book Index
Union Catalogue of Digital Books
http://97.107.129.173/logina.htm

Digital Book Index offers access "to more than 148,000 full-text digital books from more than 1,800 commercial and non-

116

commercial publishers, universities, and various private sites. More than 120,000 of these books, texts, and documents are available free, while many others are available at very modest cost." Commercial publishers include Random House, Simon & Schuster, MacMillan and Bantam Books, and aggregators such as NetLibrary and Questia are also indexed, but, as can be seen from the statistics quoted above, this remains a primary site from which to access free e-books. *As David Dillard of* Temple University notes on the home page, "One major area of difficulty in the electronic book area of publishing has been bibliographic control... A very useful resource in this area for libraries and for end users of electronic books."

In order to use the service it is necessary to log in by providing name, institution and e-mail address; this then provides direct access to the home page from which it is possible to browse by subject or author; to browse publishers' trade lists or NetLibrary by subject; or to focus on, and browse an American Studies subset. It is also possible to search by author/title, and there are also separate links to, presumably un-indexed, Foreign Language & Audio e-Books.

Browsing by subject or within American Studies takes users to finely delineated subject listings from which subject sets can be selected, while of the routes which are more likely to direct you to books for which there is a charge, browsing in NetLibrary offers Dewey categories, and browsing by publishers offers the choice of a final listing in author or title order before offering an extensive list of publishers from which to select.

Results lists are clearly set out in a tabular format with columns for author, title, edition, format(s), price ("n/c" for no charge) and publisher or organisation. Clicking on the format takes users directly to the remote site, which opens in a new window or tab and from which the book can be downloaded, read or purchased, while clicking on the publisher leads to the search engine on the publisher's site.

182.   eBook Directory, The
Various
http://www.ebookdirectory.com/

The eBook Directory claims to be "the biggest directory of free downloadable ebooks online" but access is hindered both by the clutter of advertisements around the small working area of the pages and by the automatic truncation performed on search terms ('opera' returns books on operating systems and on operating businesses). The brief introduction below the search box refers to "various categories on the left" and, on scrolling down, eleven groups are revealed beneath Google ads. and links to other pages on the site: Business; Children; Computers and Internet; Literature; Marketing; Misc. eBooks; Publishing; Recreation; Reference; Self Improvement; and Tutorials. Marketing and Self Improvement appear to be the largest categories with around 160 titles each.

Each book in the category lists appears under a title with a Rate It / Review It option to the right; beneath this is a two- or three-line publisher or author description taken from the book's parent web site, followed by a date (date added?) and the remote URL to which the *local* URL offered from the title links. This is in turn followed by the number of votes (?) and a rating. The Directory is a gateway service and the titles listed link to e-books on remote servers, in some cases to collections on remote servers; the ratings and reviews, however, are stored locally.

183.   eBook Lobby
         Various
         http://www.ebooklobby.com/

This site acts as a gateway to e-books that can be downloaded from other sources such as Godrey's Bookshelf (see) or the University of Michigan's 'Making of America' web site (see). eBook Lobby is supported by advertisements and offers e-books in 13 categories, ranging from 'Art & Photography' to 'Literature & Fiction' and 'Travel'. In all, about 400 e-books are accessible – the largest category is 'Computers and Internet'. Categories are divided into sub-categories containing lists of titles; each book title is linked to a data page containing anything from a short synopsis to full bibliographic details. Categorisation is not always reliable as Beatrix Potter's *The Roly-Poly Pudding* is found under Art & Photography|Art on the basis of its illustrations. There is no indication that e-books will be made available from third-party sites, but as a consequence of the varied sources, "Download" may produce a PDF file, a file in some other format, or an e-book in HTML/web format.

184. eBooks Just Published
Fiction
http://www.ebooksjustpublished.com/

Run by Mark Gladding in Melbourne, eBooks Just Published is an easy way to find out about new DRM-free e-books as they were released – both fiction and non-fiction, until new entries ceased in May 2010. It is important to note that DRM-free does not equate to free, so many of the books listed may have a charge; in fact, DRM-free means that it is possible to view the e-book on any device, print it any number of times, convert it to speech and make a backup copy providing only that the author's copyright is respected. The web site (in reality a blog) provides access to new e-books both through listing the ten most recently added and by way of a number of genres and sub-genres listed (with the number of titles) in the left column of the home page as well as – at the foot of the column – to a few of the highest rated titles. One of the genres is for free e-books. The body of the home page is occupied by the blog entries which review the newly added titles. Importantly – given the aim of the site – because this is a blog, all new titles, and all of the genres and sub-genres offer RSS subscriptions to that users can be alerted to new titles. There is also a weekly e-mail newsletter.

Selecting a genre brings together the relevant blog entries with the most-recently added first. Each entry includes the title, author, cover, a list of genres to which it belongs, a brief description, the number of pages, cost and a link to the remote site on which the e-book is hosted. As this is a blog entry, readers may add comments/reviews and ratings. Entries for free e-books also have a link to the site owner's own software (text2go) which will automatically download the e-book and convert it to an audiobook. Many of the free e-books come from the self-publishing site, Smashwords (*see*).

On June 26th 2010 Mark Gladding wrote, "As [users] may have realised, eBooks Just Published has been out of action for the last month or so... As the site has grown in popularity I've been unable to keep up with the steady stream of new ebook announcements....Therefore I've started working on a new application that will allow authors to create and publish their own ebook announcements on this site without requiring me to spend time editing and approving each announcement." As of January 2011, the new site has not appeared.

185. Education Portal
Various
http://education-portal.com/articles/40_Places_for_%20 College_Students_to_Find%20_Free_Unabridged_ Books%20_Online.html

This gateway does not link users directly to e-books, but to some thirty sources of free e-books such as Bartleby (*see*) or the Online Books Page (*see*).

186. eLibrary - Open eBooks Directory
Various
http://e-library.net/free-ebook.htm

Offering access to both free and charged-for e-books, the Directory describes itself as including "most of the ebooks (electronic online books) sold on the internet. Browse our collection. Find an ebook that interests you and read reviews by past readers. Clicking "visit" will take you to the ebooks seller's (or ebook author's) web site where you can buy e-books online or ask questions about the e-book contents." The site uses frames so that, in many cases, unwary users may be unaware that they have been transferred to another web site, with its own navigation.

There are well over 10,000 e-books available via the site but only about 5% of these are free. Of the free e-books a few are only available in part: there is a charge for reading further sections or chapters. There is no guarantee over what is made available: in some cases access may be only to a pamphlet, 10-page recipe collections, or lesson notes, in others it is to a multi-chapter work or the home page of a collection from which several titles can be acquired. Some works are polemical; many have self-help or quasi-religious themes.

187. ETANA: Electronic Texts and Ancient Near Eastern Archives
Near Eastern Studies
http://www.etana.org/

ETANA is "envisioned to include the permanent archiving, dissemination and generation of both front- and back-end stages of scholarly knowledge (such as archaeological excavation reports, editions of ancient and modern texts, core early monographs, dictionaries, journals, and reports in the public domain), ... [as well as] eventually an electronic publishing effort for "born digital" publications." It is digitising texts relating to ancient Near Eastern studies that have been selected as valuable for teaching and/or research. Primarily editions that are out of copyright, or for which copyright permission has been obtained are used.

In addition to some 368 core texts made directly available in PDF, the site also acts as a subject gateway to over 2,000 e-books available via the Internet Archive (*see*) and from other institutions. Both collections can be browsed by title or author lists which link to bibliographic records or directly to the text or e-book.

188. Europeana
Varied - including e-books
http://www.europeana.eu/portal/

This prototype web site provides access to paintings, music, films and books from Europe's galleries, libraries, archives and museums. In 2005 the European Commission published *i2010: communication on digital libraries,* in which it announced a strategy to promote and support the creation of a European digital library; two years later the Europeana project began. In 2010, some 74 organisations were making content available; for example, the library of the University of Ghent contributed public domain works scanned by Google. While it is not possible to search for e-books only, it is possible to refine searches by provider (library, museum, etc), country, language, date and type (image, text, video or sound). Texts may not necessarily be e-books. Access is provided by way of a detailed record which includes a link to the artifact in one of the collections.

189. Finding Free eBooks
Various
http://finding-free-ebooks.blogspot.com/

This blog of new free e-book titles – "Your source for free legal fiction " – is run by a business-woman who advertises hand-formatting e-books for Mobipocket and ePub "in return for a small fee". It is available to 'invited readers only'. As with e-Books Just Published (*see*), entries are classified by genres or categories, which are listed in the left-hand column and which serve to bring like books together. The site owner states that she is "not very good at determining genres, so if you want to suggest some for

121

particular authors, please do! And don't strictly count on my genre labels, look around at all the authors listed." However, the e-books are also usefully categorised by format so that all ePub books can be found, for example. At the time of review, there were books listed in .app (17); .doc (21); .epub (78); .fb2 (18); .html (173); .jar (23); .lit (44); .lrf (58); .mobi.prc (115); .pdb (65); .pdf (246); .rb (24); .rtf (61); .txt (55); and .ztxt (16). Once again, heavy use is made of the free e-books come from the self-publishing sites, Smashwords (*see*) and Lulu, indeed the site notes that it wishes to support independent authors, and is especially interested in linking to them.

Entries include a brief description and a cover image as well as a list of the categories to which the belong and the formats in which they are available; where the book is available from alternative sources, this is also noted.

Although the general appearance of the blog interface is cluttered, this is a useful site for locating out-of-the-way or unusual e-books, particularly those by independent authors.

190. FreeBooks4Doctors
Textbooks
http://www.freebooks4doctors.com/index.htm

Provided by the Amedeo Medical Literature Guide (http://www.amedeo.com/) and supported by Ads by Google, this gateway "was created to promote the free availability of medical books on the Internet" and provides access to 365 medical books sorted by topics (dermatology, oncology, radiology, etc). The home page notes that "Over the next years, many textbooks will be available online, free and in full-text. The unrestricted access to scientific knowledge will have a major impact on medical practice". The top twenty titles listed with cover images on the home page include the *Merck Manual of Diagnosis and Therapy* (18th edition, 2006), several titles from Médecins sans Frontières, and the 2009 Johns Hopkins University, Division of Infectious Diseases *Antibiotic Guide.*

Titles may be located by topic, language, year, rating or 'impact' (i.e. the top twenty on the site, etc) and selecting a title opens a new browser tab with the remote site/title. Some titles have a 'PDF' note beside them, and in this case the link is to the remote site where there is a further link to the title itself.

FreeBooks4Doctors is one of the sites linked to by the Open Access Textbooks Project (*see*).

191. Free Digital Textbook Initiative Gateway
Textbooks
http://clrn.org/FDTI/index.cfm

The California Learning Resource Network has a Free Digital Textbook Initiative and some 33 textbooks are listed. The initial listing shows publisher, title and – in some case – level. There is also a score for "Content Standards Met", given in the form of 'x out of y' (y varies considerably so that there, for example, are scores of 8 out of 8, 31 out of 32, and 68 out of 73). Although there is separate information about review criteria, the scoring is not explained on the site.

The title links to a full bibliographic record, which includes a brief description (including 'Purpose'), grade levels, the date it was added and the number of times viewed. A link in the form of a URL leads to the actual textbook.

192. Free e-Books
Various
http://www.e-book.com.au/freebooks.htm

On a single lengthy page, this Australian site offers access to: Best free Digital Libraries – Australia; Best free Digital Libraries - New Zealand; Best free Digital Libraries – World; Other Free Australian Books; Other Free Book Sites/Pages in English; Free Audio Books; World - Other Languages, Regional and National; Individual Topics/Miscellaneous; and Sacred Texts & Religion. A further page offers "Forgotten Books", all of which can be found at Forgottenbooks.org (only low-quality PDFs with vertical lines through all pages to prevent re-use are available free; a small charge is made for high-quality versions). Under each heading is listed a number of sources or collections with brief descriptions and web addresses.

The page explains that, "Many books in the public domain may be freely accessed here, as well as some other books under specified conditions. However we cannot offer access to any copyrighted titles unless the publisher or copyright owner has so permitted." There is also a warning about the pop-ups that may be experienced on some sites.

193. **Free Online Textbooks, Lecture Notes, Tutorials, and Videos on Mathematics**
Textbooks
http://homepages.nyu.edu/~jmg336/html/mathematics.ht
ml

The gateway provides access to software and videos, as well as e-books in the following subject areas: General Mathematics; Abstract Algebra; Analysis; Numerical Analysis; Calculus; Differential Equations; Geometry; Graph Theory; Linear Algebra & Matrices; Number Theory; Operations Research; Physics; Statistics; Miscellaneous. No provenance or selection criteria are given, but the page seems to be owned by a lecturer (an e-mail address is at the foot of the page) at New York University.

The gateway is a single web page listing resources in title order under each of the subject divisions. Most titles are listed with author(s) and a short abstract. Newly-added titles are highlighted. The book title acts as the link to the remote site.

194. **FreeTechBooks**
Textbooks
http://www.freetechbooks.com/

The site (supported by Ads by Google) offers access to computer science and programming books, textbooks and lecture notes. The home page notes that "All the books listed in this site are freely available, as they are hosted on websites that belong to the authors or the publishers... [users should] note that (a) we do not host pirated books and (b) we do not link to sites that host pirated books and (c) we do not even link to sites that link to sites that host pirated books... each author and publisher has their own terms and conditions in the forms of free / open documentation licenses, public domain or other specific ones."

Newly-added titles are listed on the home page, which also offers subject access by topics under 'Computer Science', 'Mathematics', 'Supporting Fields', 'Operating Systems', 'Programming / Scripting', 'Miscellaneous' and 'Most Popular'. By way of example, Computer Science includes 'Algorithms and Data Structures' (29 titles), 'Formal Methods' (20), 'Information Systems' (10) and 'Software Engineering' (50) as subject headings.

Initial lists are alphabetic by title, with the initial two lines of a description and indication of how many reads – although, as this is a gateway, this only indicates the number of visits to the more detailed book description. The title link leads to the fuller description (usually with excerpts) and a link to the remote site.

FreeTechBooks is one of the sites linked to by the Open Access Textbooks Project (*see*).

195. Gallica
Various
http://gallica.bnf.fr/

The French site, Gallica, claims to have over a million documents and books accessible for free, as well as maps, images, sound recordings and musical scores. It is possible to limit the search to books and, using the advanced search screen, also by language (French, English, Italian, Chinese, Spanish, German, Greek, Latin, All), subject, date and origin. There does not appear to be any means of browsing through the collection. There are sixteen partner libraries (in addition to La Bibliothèque nationale de France, BnF), and the search can also be limited by institution. The search results page lists titles with brief bibliographic details and a note of their origin and possibly also a short description and/or a cover image. Some sources offer the e-book 'subject to conditions' (e.g. leaf through for free).

Once a title is selected, the next stage seems to be dictated by the source library; for example, with BnF titles users move directly to page facsimiles in the same window/tab, while for Library of Congress titles users are presented with a an intermediate page in a new tab offering a full bibliographic description.

196. Global Text Project
Textbooks
http://globaltext.terry.uga.edu/books

A joint project of the Terry College of Business of the University of Georgia and The Daniels College of Business of the University of Denver, the Global Text Project plans to create a free library of 1,000 e-textbooks for students in developing world covering the range of topics typically encountered in a university's undergraduate programs. Their vision states that "Mass education has created tremendous opportunities and wealth for people in developed countries. It has enabled many to escape poverty, albeit a level of poverty that is not comparable to that of many in the developing nations. Mass education for the developing world is dependent among other things on finding low costs means of delivering free quality content to many. We believe we have the means for developing the necessary content and seek support to start an endeavor that can engage many for the benefit of many more. We will work through universities, world development agencies (e.g., World Bank, United Nations), and other appropriate bodies to promote adoption of the texts... Furthermore, we will work on creating a community that contributes to enhancement of the texts." All books are made available under a Creative Commons licence.

Books may be located from title listings under six subjects: Business; Computing; Education; Health; Science; and Social Science or brought together by searching on one or more of the narrower subject terms. Titles are listed with author(s) and a minimal description; they are also identified as a "Global Text book", a "Scanned book" or a "Link to another site". Those texts which are available on the Global Text site are almost all in PDF.

197.   The Online Book Page
Various
http://digital.library.upenn.edu/books/

The Online Books Page of John Mark Ockerbloom, a digital library planner and researcher at the University of Pennsylvania facilitates access to over 40,000 free e-books that are "freely readable over the Internet" – in fact the site states that the "online books listed on this page have been authored, placed online, and hosted, by a wide variety of individuals and groups throughout the world." The variety of texts is wide, and includes librettos and diaries, histories, prayer books and reference works as well as literature, textbooks and scholarly monographs – all of which may be accessed on a range of third-party sites including, for example, Project Gutenberg (*see*) and the Internet Sacred Text Archive (*see*). As access to any e-book is not directly from The Online Books Page, the means of use will vary and titles may be viewed online as HTML, facsimile page images, etc, or downloadable (possibly in several formats) depending on the host in question. Most titles listed include some bibliographic information and an indication of where the link leads.

Authors, titles and subjects (by term or Library of Congress Call Number) can all be browsed or searched, and the home page also offers a list of newly-added titles and three special collections: A Celebration of Women Writers; Banned Books Online; and Prize Winners Online. There is also a blog and a page of links to freely-available serial archives.

198.   Open Educational Resources (OER) Commons
        Textbooks
        http://www.oercommons.org/courses/material_types/text
        books

Open Educational Resources are described as "teaching and learning materials that you may freely use and reuse, without charge. OER often have a Creative Commons or GNU license that state specifically how the material may be used, reused, adapted, and shared." Supported by the William and Flora Hewlett Foundation, the Institute for the Study of Knowledge Management in Education created OER Commons in 2007 "to provide support for and build a knowledge base around the use and reuse of open educational resources." The gateway links to content on a wide range of sites, including Connexions (*see*).

Resources are organised by subject, grade level (primary, secondary and post-secondary), media type and media format, in the case of link provided here: textbooks. Searches can be limited by these criteria.

Title lists include an abstract and a note of the subject, grade, collection (source), star rating, and copyright (four categories, including "No Strings Attached" or "Remix and Share" are all explained in the right-hand column). A drop-down menu for each item allows users tag, rate, review or save the record. The title itself links directly to the remote source.

199.   Open Textbooks
        Textbooks
        http://www.studentpirgs.org/open-textbooks

This site from the US Student Public Interest Research Groups (PIRGs) offers access to 'open textbooks': "high-quality college texts offered online under a license that allows free digital access and low-cost print options. Students can read the full text free online, download a printable PDF, or purchase a hard copy at a fraction of the cost of traditional books. Also, the 'open' license typically gives instructors the flexibility to tailor the text to better fit a course by removing unneeded chapters or adding new material."

The catalogue is in the form of a single HTML page divided into sections for Accounting & Finance; Business, Management & Marketing; Computer Science & Information Systems; Economics; Humanities & Language; Mathematics & Statistics; Social Sciences; and Natural & Physical Sciences. As of late 2010, there are around 40 textbooks available. Each e-textbook record includes the title, the authors with their affiliation, the publisher (e.g. Flat World Knowledge (*see*)) and links: "details", "straight to book" and in some cases 'review'. The fuller details include an image of the book cover, a description, ISBN, courses, type of licence, biographic details of the author(s), a table of contents, links to additional resources, and a note of where the textbook is known to have been used. Purchase prices for the paper-based textbook are also given. Links take readers to the remote site.

The site contains a disclaimer: Although we have done our best to identify the highest quality texts, please remember that we are a student group and do not have the expertise to recommend materials for their academic merit.

200.   refdesk.com
Reference
http://www.refdesk.com/factency.html

As its name implies, the site aims to provide a reference service, and there are 'Fast Facts' and 'Quick Reference' sections, for example. The URL provided here takes users directly to a list of 30 encyclopaedia available for online consultation. These include *The CIA World Factbook, Britannica Online, Columbia Encyclopedia, Country Reports, Encyclopedia of Plants, My Virtual Encyclopedia,* and *Wikipedia.* Virtually all titles have a brief description following the title/link.

201.   Textbook Revolution
Various
http://textbookrevolution.org/

The text on the home page of this MediaWiki-powered site begins: "Textbook Revolution is a student-run site dedicated to increasing the use of free educational materials by teachers and professors. We want to get these materials into classrooms. Our approach is to bring all of the free textbooks we can find together in one place, review them, and let the best rise to the top and find their way into the hands of students in classrooms around the world." The term 'textbook' in the title is used loosely and here includes educational resources of all kinds (lesson notes, for example). The level is primarily, but not exclusively, undergraduate. Most referenced e-books are made available as downloadable PDF files but some can be read online as HTML web pages.

The wiki pages act as a gateway or a "repository of links" and currently textbooks may be located by subject or licence; in traditional wiki style, the pages offering access by course, topic and level have yet to be added. Subjects represented are: Biology; Business & Management; Chemistry; Computer Science & technology; Earth Sciences; Economics; Engineering; Environment; English as a Second Language; Health Sciences & Medical; Mathematics; Physics; Society and Social Sciences; Sociology; and World history. Most subject pages appear to have a US-bias. Any of these subjects lead to pages in tabular layout with columns for title, author and licence.

Clicking on a selected title takes users to a title record complete with abstract and a link to the remote site that hosts the e-textbook. Often, these are sites mentioned elsewhere in this Guide, such as Bookboon (*see*). Additional information includes the educational level and keywords; abstracts are sometimes attributed as being copied from the parent site, in other case an element of critical judgment creeps in: "... an excellent if somewhat dated...".

SEARCH ENGINES

202. Ebook-engine
Various
http://www.ebook-engine.com/

Ebook-engine claims to make finding free e-books on the Internet easier by "providing visitors with the best quality free ebook sites and pages on the web in one small search engine." The About page also notes that, "there are a couple of big free ebook site's [sic] that are full of low quality ebooks and are still getting all the market on the web which we at ebook-engine think is unfair so the larger sites are being excluded ... [in order to make] the smaller free ebook web sites more accessible for the general public." However, the site also suggests that if you cannot find your e-book using this search engine, "it is likely that you cannot download [it] for free anywhere."

The site uses Google Custom Search and is supported by 'Ads by Google'. There is no way to discover how this search engine is focused on e-books but a search on 'Emma' returned "Emma by Jane Austin" (Project Gutenberg) followed by "So's Your Aunt Emma: Lindsley Parsons : Free Download & Streaming ..." and "Anarchism and Other Essays by Emma Goldman", also from Project Gutenberg and over nine pages more, on each of which about 70% of the links were to e-books. A search for a less common word – Zenda – returned 33 sites all offering either Anthony Hope's novel or a story or play based on it.

203. Ebook Search: pdf search engine
Various
http://www.pdf-search-engine.com/

This unadorned (indeed, unadorned by any 'Help') front page claims to offer access to "> 285.000.000 Free eBooks". A simple search box is offered and results are presented in three categories: Adobe PDF files, Microsoft Word '.doc' files or PowerPoint presentations – although it is unlikely that many e-books will be found in anything other than PDF. Within these categories users take pot luck! For example a search on 'Great Expectations' offered several PDF files of the novel, as well as "Great Expectations: a guide to Alabama's High school Graduation Exam..." and "Great Expectations is a guide made to help you plan a period of study abroad..." within the first few lines. Hovering over each title in the list produces a 2-line description, apparently taken from the file itself.

The site also offers an eBook Search Firefox Toolbar, and is supported by Ads by Google, and care is needed to avoid leaving the search engine for another apparent e-book collection.

204. Ebook Search Engine.com
Various
http://www.ebook-search-engine.com/

Although this is a different interface from Ebook-engine (*see*), it has the same comment with the same refractory apostrophe ("there are a couple of big free ebook site's [sic] that are full of low quality ebooks..."), which – although in this case the comment is on the front page beneath the search box – suggests the same origin. However, Ebook Search Engine.com offers searches that can be limited by language and/or by PDF or Word .DOC and appears to result in a higher number of hits.

As with 'Ebook Search: pdf search engine' (*see*), hovering over titles in the results list produces a 2-line description, apparently taken from the file itself, and the site is supported by Ads by Google, positioned so that care is needed to avoid leaving the search engine for another apparent e-book collection.

205.   Inkmesh
Mostly fiction
http://inkmesh.com/

Inkmesh is an e-book search engine that both makes it easy to find free e-books, and offers the facility to compare e-book prices for the Kindle, iPhone, Sony Reader, Nook, etc. The 'About' page lets users know which sites are included in searches (e.g. Amazon.com, FictionWise (*see*), Project Gutenberg (*see*), Waterstone's and W H Smith).

The front page offers a search box – with examples and choice of searching free e-books or all e-books – and the option of browsing by subject (e.g. Adventure, Business, Romance). There is also direct access to "Promotional Free eBooks" for the Sony Books, Kindle Books, Nook Books, Smashword Books, Baen Books, and All Free Ebooks.

A simple search by title, author or keyword produces (as you type) suggested searches, and ultimately a multi-page listing of titles, complete with books covers, ratings, keywords, devices, the first two lines of the publisher's description and – should you search for all e-books – prices. In the left-hand margin is the possibility to limit the results by star rating, price, device and language, as well as by excluding public domain e-books and by type of e-book (audiobook, for example). A search for free e-books produces a similar page; clicking on a title produces a link to the source or sources (e.g. the Internet Archive). All pages of the site offer a chance to leave feedback or ideas for improvements.

Inkmesh also tweets regularly about e-book matters and new titles.

206.   Luzme
Various
http://luzme.com/

Originally named eBookPrice.Info, Luzme currently searches the twenty e-book stores listed on the home page, and offers searching by author, title, ISBN (recognising both 10- and 13-digit versions), series or keyword. It is possible to set a 'preferred country' for searches (US, UK, Canada or Europe).

The keyword search is a little slow but return matches and partial matches against both authors and titles. A simple author search results in a page with the various covers of his or her books, and selecting a cover takes you to a page that begins with a summary of best prices for each format (PC, Mac, Sony, Nook, iPhone, Blackberry, Palm, Android, Book and Audio) and a summary description of the book, followed by a series of tables – one for each format – listing the various vendors. The tables have columns for vendor, price (given in dollars or pounds), format, when the price was checked (during the review this was mostly given as "today" or "yesterday" although a few slightly older dates were also apparent), geographical restrictions and comments (future discounts, club price, etc). Clicking on the vendor takes users directly to the vendor's page for the book in question (this may seem obvious, but sometimes such a link would simply go to the vendor and the user would have to perform the search again).

207.   OverDrive Digital Media Locator
Various
http://search.overdrive.com/

This slightly different offering locates e-books at bookstores or libraries. It is powered by OverDrive, the US-based e-book supplier for libraries – especially public libraries – that is rapidly becoming a force in the UK. In addition to book searches, it is possible to search directly for bookstores and libraries (OverDrive clients only, so a little limited at present in the UK).

Simple searches may be conducted using author, title, keyword or ISBN while the advanced search form adds subject, media format, publisher, imprint and language. Results from a search are listed with cover image, author, publisher and format (e.g. 'OverDrive MP3 Audiobook', 'Adobe PDF eBook' or 'Microsoft eBook'); beside each is one or more buttons: 'Find at a

132

bookstore', 'Find at a library', or 'WorldCat' (which returns the catalogue record).

Free e-books can be located in OverDrive libraries using the following screen by selecting a country (some editions may not be available in the UK) and a region (or by using a 5-digit US postal code).

208.   PDFse Ebook Search
Various
http://pdfse.com/

The search box offers access by author's name, book title or topic and a 'Find Ebooks' button, while the lower portion of the page suggests that users could "get inspired by other people's searches" by way of a tag cloud of search terms, which can be narrowed by selecting an initial letter. Searches return a list (the second slot is reserved for an Ad by Google) showing author/title, the beginning of a description and a URL for each title.

Test searches suggest that searches are only restricted by format (PDF) and little further restricting to e-books is apparent – lists included a publisher's catalogue, a transcription of a Second Life Q&A session, several scholarly papers (including one which was behind the journal publisher's password access), and book reviews – in fact, none of the test searches located an actual e-book!

Part 2: Descriptions: Younger than Adult e-Books

209.   BBC – Dr Who
Collection
Leisure Science fiction
http://www.bbc.co.uk/doctorwho/classic/ebooks/

The BBC has made available eight "rare and acclaimed" Dr Who novels as e-books. They may be read online or downloaded. Some, but not all, have to be read online on a page-by-page basis. All include, or have available alongside, the original artwork and author notes.

210.   Children's Books Online: the Rosetta Project
Collection
Children's fiction
http://www.editec.net/

The project believes itself to be the largest collection of illustrated antique books on line. It is an "online library of illustrated books [which] is a volunteer-driven project. It has grown slowly since 1996 from the work of a single man and a handful of books, to a vibrant volunteer-driven organization publishing new books and translations every week."

Apart from multimedia books, audio books and books in more than one language, the collection is divided by age: pre-reader and very early readers; early readers; intermediate readers; advanced readers; and adult readers. There is also a master index and search engine for combinations of title, author, illustrator, publisher and date.

Selecting a title from any of the collections produces a page of thumbnail images of the cover and of each double-page spread, from which a starting point can be selected – the book is then read on high-quality double-page facsimiles, complete with original illustrations. The top of every page screen is headed with the book details (e.g. *Alice's Adventures In Wonderland* / aiw45 | by Lewis Carroll; illustrated by John Tenniel; published by DeWolfe, Fiske & Co. | 1901) and arrows above and below the page image take you to adjacent page images or back to the index page. From every page it is also possible to buy the complete e-book as a single file.

135

211.   Children's Logos Library
Archive
Various multilingual
http://www.logoslibrary.eu/owa-wt/new_wordthe
que.main_bimbi?lang=en

The Children's Logos Library does not have the textual search function of the Logos Library (*see*) but offers lists of titles in each of 36 languages through an interface designed to appeal to children. At the time of review there were just over 100 English-language titles and just over 540 in Italian (its home country) – most other languages have fewer titles. As the Logos Group is known for its translation services, it is unsurprising that some titles, such as those by Hans Christian Andersen, appear in many of the languages.

Selecting a country produces a simply author/title list, and selecting a book produces a display in which the text is presented in a central column masquerading as a book page, with back, forward and start buttons. As with the Logos Library, the column is narrow, so that there are often irregular line breaks followed by one-word, or very short, lines. Again, books may be downloaded – but in this case the button is easily mistaken for a link to the next page!

212.   Classic Book Library
Collection
Fiction
http://classicbook.info/

** Site reported as unavailable January 2011 **

The Classic Book Library is a free online library "containing treasured classics for old and young alike." The Library is divided into seven collections: Historical Fiction; Romance; Children's Literature; History; Science Fiction; Science; and Mystery. The collections can be browsed from the Java-script menu at the top of every page. "From the menu, you can browse all books in any genre, go to the Table of Contents, or jump straight to any chapter. The chapters are divided into separate pages, making it easier for anyone to bookmark exactly where they were in each book!"

Books in each category are listed by title; a selected title is first shown as an HTML table of contents, and then as a series of

136

short screen pages, with links to previous and next pages. At the top of each page is a bread-crumb trail, allowing easy access to the table of contents, the collection or the Library's home page, as well as a note of the page being read (Page x of xx).

There are some 30 titles for children, ranging from *Anne of Green Gables* to *The Wonderful Wizard of Oz*.

213.   DQ Books
Experimental publishing
Graphic novels
http://www.dqbooks.com/

This is a collection of four short artist- or graphic-books, although while the site is called 'DQ Books' the text uses the terms 'magazine' and 'issues' in noting that new releases will be infrequent. Some of the volumes contain sexually explicit images and one deals with drugs. They can be viewed in a series of double-page spreads to the accompaniment of music, using Adobe Flash to present the page images. The books/issues are: *Invasion* ("Seven days of graphic improvisation: Capitalist invasion and mixed techniques."); *Seasons* ("16 illustrators, artists and photographers invent the life of a woman according to seasons. Mixed techniques."); *Where is the party?* ("Brazillian, Italian and French artists for a narcotic party, carried out with blue Bic ™ pen"); and *Beneath a steel sky* ("From Brooklyn to Central Park beneath a steel sky. Analog photography by Festo").

The authors describe the collection as: "a variable geometry project born from a four hands graphic improvisation: Festo (1hOS.com) meets Telmolindo (telmolindo.com) in "Invasion". Artists, illustrators and photographers will join [joined] the team in the second issue ("Seasons") for a sixteen people collaboration. Interdisciplinary "cadoure exquis" game, artists involved follow the rules of imposed theme and technique in an impromptu narration. French composer Avril created the original soundscapes."

214.   Eco Zoo
Experimental publishing
Children's pop-up books
http://www.ecodazoo.com/

Eco Zoo is a series of English/Japanese pop-up books introduced as promoting a sometimes rather obscure green, clean environment message: "The Eco Zoo... If you take a close look at the animals there you might be able to get some tips to live in a more environmentally friendly way". The short pop-up books are cleverly presented to the song of jungle-birds.

215.   Grimm's Fairy Tales
Single title
Literature
http://www-2.cs.cmu.edu/~spok/grimmtmp/

This is a basic HTML book containing the 209 fairy tales collected by the brothers Grimm. Curiously, the introduction notes that the exact print source is unknown: "The etext appears to be based on the translation by Margaret Hunt called *Grimm's Household Tales*, but it is not identical to her edition. (Some of the translations are slightly different, the arrangement also differs, and the Grimm's scholarly notes are not included.)" The collection is offered in the original order with each tale on a separate page.

Tales are printed unadorned with illustrations or by formatting.

216.   Hans Christian Andersen
Archive
Fiction
http://hca.gilead.org.il/

The original translations into English of Hans Christian Andersen's 168 fairy tales was by H P Paull in 1872, and 140 of them are available in this collection. According to the introduction, this hypertext version is based both on an e-text found in the Andersen Homepage of the Danish National Literary Archive and on Mrs. Paull's nineteenth century translation, which is now in the public domain. The Danish National Literary Archive text is 'Danish Popular Legends' – "first published in *The Riverside Magazine for Young People*, Vol. IV, pp. 470-474, New York, October 1870, [and] never published in Denmark". All 168 tales are list chronologically on the home page.

Clicking on a title takes you to an individual page for the fable, in plain text across the complete screen width with black print against a grey background lightly illustrated by a repeat reproduction of a paper cutting made by Andersen of a Pierrot carrying a tray of object representing his own life. It is possible to switch off the background. At the foot of each tale are three arrows: back to the chronological list of titles, or to the previous and next titles. The initial letter of each tale is embellished by a small illustration.

217.   International Children's Digital Library (ICDL)
Collection
Children's fiction
http://www.icdlbooks.org/

The summary mission of the International Children's Digital Library Foundation is given as "to support the world's children in becoming effective members of the global community - who exhibit tolerance and respect for diverse cultures, languages and ideas -- by making the best in children's literature available online free of charge." Since its launch in November 2002, the Library had developed to offer free access to some 4,444 exemplary works in 54 languages from more than 42 countries. It can be accessed for free in 11 languages with "innovative software that was developed by hearing from young people about their needs, interests, and capacities". The goal is to create a collection of more than 10,000 books in at least 100 languages. ICDL relies on the international participation of libraries, publishers, authors and illustrators to insure that the collection grows by donating copyright-cleared books. It is now also available as an iPad application.

An advanced search facility allows for searching by keywords in one of the many languages, or limiting by criteria grouped under audience, appearance, content, type and subject. However the fun, children's simple search interface allows criteria such as the colour of the cover, the type of characters (e.g. real animals, imaginary creatures), short / medium / long books, make-believe or true, mood (happy or sad),or type of story (e.g. action / adventure or funny / humourous). As criteria are added by clicking on the buttons, the number of thumb-nail covers in the centre of the screen reduces. Clicking on a title produces a simple page of details, including a cover image, and links from the author's name, to other books like the one chosen and to reviews by other children. There are three ways of reading a book: the defaults plus 'comic' and 'spiral' – in the default mode a 'contents page' of double-page thumbnail images acts as a starting point. Selecting a double page, produces a two-page facsimile, on which the text or the whole page can be magnified. Navigation to the next or previous page is by clicking on a pair of arrows or on the left or right page.

218.   L Lee Lowe Online Fiction
*See also: **Mortal Ghost** and **Corvus***
Single titles
Short stories
http://lleelowe.com/short-stories/

L Lee Lowe's young adult fiction (see also *Mortal Ghost* and *Corvus*) is exemplified by the six short stories available here. All are tightly written tense and challenging; all make for good reading. Each can be downloaded in PDF or read on the screen.

219.   Magic Keys: Children's Story Books Online
Collection
Children's literature
http://www.magickeys.com/books/

The site, supported by Ads by Google, offers illustrated children's stories for children of all ages, divided into sets for young children, older children and young adult; some have read-aloud (word-by-word and/or page) audio tracks. At the time of review there were just over 30 titles. The catalogue is on one long page and titles have a cover image and an icon to show if audio is available, as well as a one-sentence description.

Each title offers access to the author's and artist's biographies. Stories are divided into a number of scrollable HTML pages, and from the foot of each page there is the possibility of moving directly to a page, of moving forward or backwards by a page, or of returning to the top of the page. Copyright on each story is usually reserved to the author.

220. *Mortal Ghost* and *Corvus*
See also: **L Lee Lowe Online Fiction**
Social e-books
Novels
http://lleelowe.com/

These two full length novels from L Lee Lowe were written chapter by chapter in a blog, in order to facilitate comments from his readers. The books are free to be read chapter by chapter online or downloaded as a PDF file (or chapter files) and, now they are completed, may also be purchased in hardcopy. Both are also available as weekly podcasts while *Mortal Ghost* is also available in audiobook format. Each chapter comprises a single long scrollable page. All the fiction available from this site carries a Creative Commons Attribution-Noncommercial-No Derivative Works License.

Both titles received reader accolades while they were being delivered via the blog, a new chapter each week. Both are tense, psychological thrillers.

221.   Spartacus: Encyclopedia of the First World War
Single titles
Encyclopaedia/Textbooks
http://www.spartacus.schoolnet.co.uk/FWW.htm

Although difficult to navigate, this text-book-come-encyclopedia offers a wealth of information linked to excerpts from primary material. As a born-digital e-book, it does not expect users to read it linearly and this may account for the compilers choice of the terms encyclopedia in its title. The heavy use of advertising and links to relevant books on Amazon can be distracting but the extensive content rewards those who persevere! It is intended for use in schools.

Access is by way of a two-part table of contents. Firstly there are sections on Chronology; Outbreak of War; Allied Armed Forces; Central Powers; Important Battles; Technology; Political Leaders; British Home Front; Military Leaders; Trench War; The Soldiers; and Major Offensives. These are followed by a link to First World War Digital Archive, and a second table with links to War at Sea; War in the Air; War Artists; War Literature; War Heroes; Women at War; Organisations; Strategies & Tactics; Weapons & Machines; Inventors and the War; Theatres of War; and War

Statistics. Many of these point to a second list of links and thus onwards to text pages.

The content is presented in HTML pages – some short and others more lengthy. All contain further links to other pages within the encyclopedia, and in some case there is primary material following the text. For example, following the entry on the British Expeditionary Force there are two journalists' description – one from the *Manchester Guardian* of 18th August, 1914. Following each entry are also some further potentially useful links, but care must be taken as not all are internal.

The Second World War, which follows a similar pattern, and further historical and other textbooks are also available from the home page of this site.

222.   Stories from the Web
Collection
Children's fiction
http://www.storiesfromtheweb.org/sfwhomepage.htm

The site contains a selection of stories and activities for various age groups but is now a charged-for site with subscriptions for schools, libraries and families. A family membership costs £36 per year or £3.50 per month. All children and young people from 0 to 14 in the family are covered by a membership.

The promotion on the website notes that Stories from the Web is about storytelling, creative writing, books and reading, games, and 'making and drawing' for toddlers to teenagers. It is a safe, fully-moderated website with staff who are all CRB checked.

223.   Wikijunior
Collection
Non-fiction
http://en.wikibooks.org/wiki/Wikijunior

The home page states that the "aim of this project is to produce age-appropriate non-fiction books for children from birth to age 12. These books are richly illustrated with photographs, diagrams, sketches, and original drawings. Wikijunior books are produced by a worldwide community of writers, teachers, students, and young people all working together. The books present factual information that is verifiable. You are invited to join in and write, edit, and rewrite each module and book to improve its content. Our books are distributed free of charge under the terms of the Creative Commons Attribution-ShareAlike License."

The bookshelf on the front page shows fifteen books ranging from *Ancient Civilizations* through *Big Cats* and *Geometry* to *US Charters of Freedom*. There are also a number of 'pre-readers' based on the alphabet and numbers. It is the nature of a wiki that it will contain pages that are ready for publication, as well as pages that are being prepared and some which are 'stubs' – identified as needed, and Wikijunior is no different. There is material in a range of languages apart from English.

Late Entries

224.   Machine of Death
Single title
Short stories
http://machineofdeath.net/a/ebook

This description is taken verbatim from the 'About' pages. *"Machine of Death* is an upcoming published anthology of short stories edited by Ryan North, Matthew Bennardo, and David Malki !, inspired by [an] episode of Ryan's Dinosaur Comics. From January 15, 2007, through April 30, 2007, we actively solicited short story submissions for the book. Submissions were free and open to everybody. Ryan, Matt and David ! have chosen their favorite stories from the nearly 700 submissions, and each contributor has been paid for each story selected.

Each contributor to the book has the right to purchase copies of the book at wholesale and will be free to resell the book however they like and keep their profits.

On November 2, 2010, the manuscript was placed online, in PDF form, licensed under a Creative Commons Attribution-Noncommercial-Share Alike 3.0 license. That means people will be able to read, copy, and distribute all the stories for free, which will expose more readers to the material, thus building awareness and driving physical sales. There is also an audiobook version, which is being released weekly as a free podcast."

225.   Africana Books Collection
Archives and Collections
Various
https://www.up.ac.za/dspace/handle/2263/4911

This small collection of Africana has been scanned and deposited in the University of Pretoria repository, UPSpace. Searchable and browsable by title, author and subject, the collection comprises 116 titles published between 1731 and 1932. It includes titles in French, Dutch and English – for example, *A brief account of Bushman folklore and other texts; Eight months in an ox-waggon; or A guide to the gold fields of South Africa, with map.* The subject index begins with Dewey Decimal class numbers and continues with an alphabetic sequence of subject terms. Books are listed with year of publications, the full title and author(s) including dates of birth and death where these are known; cover images are included in some cases.

In the normal way of institutional repositories, selecting a title produces a full bibliographic record, including at its foot, links to download sections of the book – in this case usually of 50 pages in length in PDF. Facsimile pages are of good quality.

226.   Planet PDF: Free PDF eBooks Archive
See also: **Planet eBook** (82)
Archives and Collections
Classic literature
http://www.planetpdf.com/free_pdf_ebooks.asp

Part of the larger Planet PDF site and closely linked to the larger Planet eBook sister site, this archive of classical works is listed on a single web page beginning with *A Christmas Carol* and *A Tale of Two Cities* and ending with *Wuthering Heights*. In between are works by Austin, Joyce, Milton, Stevenson, Tolstoy, Wells and Wilde, among others – some 65 titles in all. In each case the title is followed by a short extract but only occasionally by the author.

Selecting a title moves the reader onto a single page containing a longer extract from the start of the book and links to download a PDF and a 'tagged PDF' version of the text. Downloads are fast and deliver a single file containing the whole book, with bookmarks to parts and chapters in a contents page to the left of the text.

227.   Dear Monsieur Picasso
Single title
Art
http://zonezero.com/exposiciones/fotografos/baldwin/

The book is described by Dan Colman on his 'Open Culture' blog (http://www.openculture.com) as follows. "In the summer of 1955, Frederick Baldwin, a college student at Columbia University, set out on a pilgrimage of sorts, hoping to meet Pablo Picasso. Baldwin traveled first to Le Havre (presumably by boat), then headed south, down to Vallauris and Cannes, until he eventually reached Picasso's home on the Riviera, known as Villa la Californie. It took a little craftiness and moxie, but the young American gained entrance into Picasso's studio." Baldwin lost the manuscript of his diary, but later relocated it and a 22-page except with many photographs of Picasso is the result.

228.   Figment
Self publishing
Various
http://figment.com/

Figment is described as "a community where you can share your writing, connect with other readers, and discover new stories and authors. Whatever you're into, from sonnets to mysteries, from sci-fi stories to cell phone novels, you can find it all here." Short stories or novella can be restricted so that they can only be read by the author, or the author and friends and family, or can be made completely public. Figment was co-founded by Dana Goodyear, a staff writer at *The New Yorker,* and Jacob Lewis, the former Managing Editor at *The New Yorker* and Condé Nast Portfolio.

229.   Google eBooks
See also: **Google Books** (50)
Archives and Collections
Various
http://books.google.com/ebooks

Google eBooks allows users to acquire and access e-books, no matter where they are. Google eBooks stores a user's library in "the digital cloud", so that they can be read anywhere on any device (iPad, iPhone, Android, laptop, etc) with an Internet connection, in each case seamlessly picking up from the page reading was left, regardless of device. e-Books may be purchased from the Google eBookstore, or from a number of independent booksellers and retail partners. At the end of 2010, purchase was not yet available in the UK and the message "The latest Google eBooks are not available for sale in your location, yet... Google is working with publishers around the world to let you buy the latest ebooks from top authors. In the meantime, you can still browse millions of free and public domain Google eBooks and read them effortlessly across your devices" was being displayed. Google eBooks offers access to some three million free e-books although there seems to be no way of searching only for free titles. The front page has a 'Best of free' link and searching for 'free' produces a limited selection.

Selecting a title leads to a bibliographic description, complete with reviews, ratings and 'Related books', and links to 'Get it now' or 'View sample' or 'Read on your device' – using the first of these transfer the title to 'My Google eBooks' and offers a 'Continue shopping' or a 'Read the book now' button. The latter produces facsimile pages with options for continuous text or change of font size. The Google eBooks application is not available for UK users as of the end of 2010 so reading is limited to PCs and laptops.

230. Local Knowledge Online (LKO)
Search engine
Various
http://www.localko.com/

This e-book search engine allows users "to search, discover, preview, buy and subscribe to e-books and e-reference works that they don't know about or cannot access". It is currently set up to search across Amazon Books, Credo Reference and Google Books (*see*) and a search can be directed to one source or 'All content'. At the search stage it is possible to tick boxes for 'Subscribe', 'Purchase', 'Limited preview', 'Full view' (meaning "Titles with free viewing for all pages" or free e-books), or 'My content' – titles in collections to which a user already subscribes. In December 2010 it was not possible to search for free e-books despite the search option but the feature is in the process of being added.

Results are returned under four tabs for the full search and each of the three constituent sources, with possible limiting factors to be applied to the results (author, year, keywords, publishers) available in the left-hand column. Each title has a cover image, topic, collection, keywords and an extract around the search term, as well as links to its parent collection(s).

231. BookYap
Search engine
Various
http://bookyap.com/

BookYap is a search engine linked to Amazon.com and does not claim to offer any free e-books at this time, nor indeed is it limited to e-books; but it does provide quite a number of titles priced at less than a dollar. Searches can be conducted from the home page or users can move directly to titles for one of 25 groups of readers: Alpha Male, History Buff, Parent, etc. Once an initial selection has been made, covers with star ratings and pop-up descriptions fill most of the page – to their left is a panel which allows advanced filtering. If the original choice was by reader group, it is possible to 'switch off' some of the keywords used, but more importantly, it is also possible to exclude print books and limit finds to a price range. Books for 'thrill seekers' found 10,677 titles, which reduced to 3,064 e-books; limiting the cost to minimum to one further reduced this number to 452, including titles by John Grisham, Harlan Coben and Stephen King. Selecting a title produced a page with a full description and price information; deciding to purchase takes users to Amazon. Clicking the thumbs up or thumbs down icon against selections enables BookYap to learn your likes and dislikes and improve future recommendations.

BookYap is a social tool as well as a search engine and allows reviews and recommendations to be published on the site or over any social network such as Facebook.

Kindle, iPhone and iPad applications will be available soon.

232.   Globusz *and* **Bibliotastic**
Self Publishing
Various
http://www.globusz.com/
http://www.bibliotastic.com/

Globusz, and its sister site Bibliotastic, both allow authors to publish books which are then made freely available on the site; Globusz also makes available a number of out-of-copyright titles by established authors such as Bertrand Russell, Lubbock and Thoreau. On both sites it is possible to browse by author or by way of categories (for both fiction and non-fiction) and in each case a brief description and cover image are presented prior to the full title. Globusz offers browsing online or downloads in a software/application format (.exe) as well as – occasionally, in PDF, while Bibliotastic offers the same online browsing format plus downloads in Kindle, ePub, PDF, Mobi and PRC formats. Bibliotastic also allows registered users to review titles.

The browsing format displays page by page, with arrows to move forward or backwards in the chapter and a hovering link to the contents page. Pages require scrolling and include images where available.

Both Globusz and Bibliotastic are run by teams of volunteers "located in the USA, UK and Australasia. Our goal is to create and operate the premier source for free, contemporary, e-books on the web. [It provides] a great platform for new and evolving authors to reach a wide audience and for readers to give them direct feedback."

General Index

Item number:

Africana	225
Amazon	28, 54, 65, 70, 75, 88, 102, 153, 175, 179, 205, 221, 230, 231
Amazon *See also* Kindle	
Andersen, Hans Christian	51, 216
Antiquarian	19, 68
Archives	1-107, 225, 226
Art	136, 142, 227
Asia	4
Athabasca University Press	150
Austen, Jane	58
Australia	137
Barsky, Robert F	138
Benkler, Yochai	174
Bible	9
Biodiversity	10, 94, 143
Biography	138, 227
Blake, William	11
Botany	18, 53, 72, 68
Brooks, Kevin	159
Canada	32, 61
Carlyle, Thomas	21
Celtic Studies	22
Children literature	91, 219
Children's Pop-up Books	214
Children's Fiction	44, 170, 210, 211, 212, 215, 216, 217, 218, 219, 220, 222
China	24
Chomsky, Noam	138
Classical Genetics	35
Classical Medicine	107
Classics	26, 28, 81, 82, 226, 229
Colman, Dan	227
Collections	1-107, 225, 226, 229
Computer Gaming	135, 166
Computing	163
Conference Proceedings	121
Cooking	141
Country Studies	60, 139
Courseware *See* Textbooks	
Cumming, Charles	159
Darwin, Charles	3, 23

Defence	118
Dictionary	137, 142
Discovery	202-208, 230
Doctorow, Cory	148
Education	55, 150
Encyclopaedia	136, 137, 142, 143, 144, 151, 152, 153, 154, 164, 173, 176, 221
Esposito, Joseph J	172
Europe	188
Fantasy Novels	111
Fiction	17, 39, 40, 51, 66, 27, 95, 179, 184, 206, 212, 216, 224, 232
Fiction *See also* Literature; Novels; Science Fiction	
Fitzpatrick, Kathleen	171
French, Nicci	159
Gateways	178-201
Genetics	35
Geography	60, 139
Google	50, 229
Graphic Novels	157, 213
Gregory, John	147
Grimm, Brothers	146, 215
Hamid, Mohsin	159
Handbooks	37, 60, 128
Health	35, 53, 107, 127, 128, 155, 190
Herbalism	53
History	61, 65, 113, 153
Humanities	1, 57, 78, 85, 86, 99
India	31
Institutional Repositories	225
iPad / iPhone	85, 96, 108, 109, 134, 203, 206, 229, 231
Jones, Susanna	156
Joseph, Chris	165
Kindle	5, 38, 56, 70, 71, 85, 88, 98, 133, 206, 231, 232
Kindle *See also* Amazon	
Leadbetter, Charles	175
Learned Society Publishers	127-128
Lessing, Dorothy	167
LibriVox	88

Literature 11, 26, 28, 29, 42, 62, 63, 75, 79, 82, 89, 90, 92, 93, 100, 102, 103, 104, 116, 119, 146, 167, 215, 226

Literature *See also* Fiction; Novels; Science Fiction

Litt, Toby 159

Lowe, L Lee 170, 218, 220

MacLeod, Alison 156

Manuscripts 3, 58

Mason, Matt 159

Mathematical 54, 121, 149, 193

Medicine 107, 127, 128, 155, 190

Monographs 47, 54, 113, 114, 115, 118, 121, 126, 135, 140, 147, 150, 161, 163, 166, 168, 171, 172, 174, 175, 177

Multilingual 64, 211

Near Eastern Studies 36, 187

Near Eastern Studies *See also* Oriental Studies

Nook Reader 203, 206

Noon, Jeff 156

Nordic Literature 87

Novels 108, 132, 148, 156, 157, 160, 165, 167, 170, 220

Novels *See also* Fiction; Literature; Science Fiction

Novik, Naomi 173

Nygren, David 158

Oriental Studies 77

Oriental Studies *See also* Near Eastern Studies

Out-of-print 14

Philosophy 55

Picasso, Pablo 227

Poe, Edgar Allan 29

Poetry 83, 95, 108, 110

Politics 55

Pop-up Books 214

Poynder, Richard 161

Professional Bodies 127-128

Psychology 55

Publisher Gateways 129-131

Publishers 129, 130, 131

Publishers, Mainstream 108-112

Publishing, Experimental 156-159

Pullinger, Kate 165

Reference	7, 53, 139, 141, 200
Religion	9, 20, 25, 37, 57, 80, 168
Reports	127, 128
Rossignol, Jim	135
Scandinavian/Nordic Literature	87
Scholarly	44, 77, 117, 120, 123, 145, 171, 177
Science Fiction	5, 8, 111, 209
Scotland	47
Search Engines	202-208, 230, 231
Self Publishing	132-134, 228, 232
Single Titles	135-155, 224, 227
Shakespeare, William	92, 102, 103, 104
Shaw, William	156
Short Stories	108, 158, 159, 218, 224
Social Reading	13, 59, 162
Social e-Books	160-177
Sociology	55
Sony Reader	69, 71, 85, 203, 206
Stark, Jonathan	163
Stephens, Michael	168, 177
Textbooks	12, 30, 41, 48, 67, 73, 74, 76, 84, 96, 101, 109, 149, 153, 155, 180, 190, 191, 193, 194, 196, 198, 199, 221
Travel	147
Trench, William F.	149
Union Catalogue of Digital Books	181
University Presses	113-126
USA	140, 144, 145, 151, 154
Victoriana	100
Volumes of Letters	21
Wales	14
Wark, McKenzie	166
Wikis	67, 101, 141, 143, 160, 164, 173, 174, 176, 201, 223
Yudu	42, 103

Title Index

Item number:

217 Babel Street	156
A Million Penguins	160
ADB	137
Africana Books Collection	225
Alex Catalogue of Electronic Texts	1
American Memory	2
American Museum of Natural History Darwin Manuscripts Project	3

See also: Charles Darwin Online, Complete Works of

Artcyclopedia	136
Asian Classics Input Project	4
Assayer, The	178
Australian Dictionary of Biography (ADB)	137
Badosa	108
Baen Free Library	5
Bartleby	6
Bartleby Reference	7
BBC – Dr Who	8, 209
Bible Gateway	9
Bibliotastic	232
Biodiversity Heritage Library	10
Blake Archive	11
Book Glutton	13, 162
Bookboon	12
Books from the Past	14
BookServer (Internet Archive)	15
Books-On-Line	179
BookYap	231
Bookyards	16
Bored.com	17
Botanicus	18
British Library: Turning the Pages™	19
BuddhaNet's eBook Library	20
Building iPhone Apps with HTML, CSS, and JavaScript	163
Carlyle Letters Online	21
CELT: Corpus of Electronic Texts	22
Charles Darwin Online, Complete Works of	23

See also: American Museum of Natural History Darwin
Manuscripts Project

Children's Logos Library	211
Children's Story Books Online (Magic Keys)	219
Children's Books Online: the Rosetta Project	210
Chinese Literature Classics	24
Chomsky: A Life of Dissent	138
Christian Classics Ethereal Library	25
CIA World Fact Book	139

Citizendium 164
    See also: Wikipedia
City Sites 140
Classic Book Library 27, 212
Classic Bookshelf 28
Classic Reader 90
ClassicAuthors 26
Cliffs Notes 109
Collected Works of Edgar Allan Poe 29
Columbia University Press: gutenberg<e> 113
Community College Open Textbook Collaboration 180
Connexions (Rice University Press) 30
Cookbook 141
Corpus of Electronic Texts 22
Corvus 170, 220
Darwin Online *see* Charles Darwin Online, Complete Works of
Dear Monsieur Picasso 227
Dictionary of Art Historians 142
Digital Book Index 181
Digital Library of India 31
digitalculturebooks 114
DQ Books 157, 213
Dr Who 8, 209
Dumbarton Oaks Research Library 115
Early Canadiana Online 32
eBook Crossroads: Directory of ePublishers 129
eBook Directory, The 182
eBook Lobby 183
Ebook Search Engine.com 204
Ebook Search: pdf search engine 203
Ebook-engine 202
eBookPrice.Info 206
eBooks Just Published 184
eBooks@Adelaide 33
Eco Zoo 214
Education Portal 185
Electronic Texts and Ancient Near Eastern Archives 187
eLibrary - Open eBooks Directory 186
ELT Press: University of North Carolina Greensboro English
    Department 116
Encyclopedia of Life (EOL) 143
Encyclopedia of the First World War (Spartacus) 153, 221
Encyclopedia Smithsonian 144
EOL 143
eReader.com 34
ESP (Electronic Scholarly Publishing) 35
ETANA: Electronic Texts and Ancient Near Eastern Archives 36, 187
Europeana 188

Evangelical Library 37
Every Writer's Resource: Ebook Publishers 130
FanFiction 132
Feedbooks 38
Fiction.us 39
FictionWise 40
Figment 228
Finding Free eBooks 189
Flat World Knowledge 41
Flight Paths: A networked novel 165
Founders Constitution 145
Free Digital Textbook Initiative Gateway 191
Free e-Book Library on Yudu 42
Free e-Books 192
Free Online Textbooks, Lecture Notes, Tutorials, and Videos on
    Mathematics 193
FreeBooks4Doctors 190
Free-ebooks.net 43
FreeTechBooks 194
Froebel Archive Digital Collection 44
    See also Roehampton University Children's Literature
    Collection
FullBooks.com 45
GAIA: Global, Area and International Archive (University
    of California) 117
Gallica 195
Gamer Theory 166
Get Free eBooks 46
Glasgow Digital Library Ebooks 47
Global Text Project 48, 196
Global, Area and International Archive 117
Globusz 232
Godfreys Book-shelf 49
Golden Notebook Project 167
Google Books 50
Google eBooks 229
Grimm's Fairy Tales 146, 215
Gutenberg *see* Columbia University Press: gutenberg<e>
    see Project Gutenberg
Hans Christian Andersen 51, 216
Harvey Cushing/John Hay Whitney Medical Historical Library 107
HathiTrust 52
Henrietta's Herbal 53
Historical Mathematics Collection 54
Holy of Holies: On the Constituents of Emptiness 168
    See also: Without Gods: Towards a History of Disbelief
How to see the World 147
ICDL 217

Ideology.us   55
Inkmesh   205
Institute for National Strategic Studies   118
International Children's Digital Library (ICDL)   217
Internet Archive   15, 56, 75, 98
Internet Sacred Text Archive   57
Jane Austen's Fiction Manuscripts   58
L Lee Lowe Online Fiction   170, 218, 220
Libertary: Freedom of the Book   59, 169
Library of Congress Country Studies   60
Library of Western Fur Trade Historical Source Documents   61
Lida Quillen's ePublishers List   131
Literature Network   62
Literature Project   63
Little Brother   148
Llyfrau O'r Gorffennol *see* Books from the Past
Local Knowledge Online (LKO)   230
Logos Library   64
LuEsther T. Mertz Library Rare Book Digitization Project   72
Luzme   206
Machine of Death   224
Magic Keys: Children's Story Books Online   219
Making of America   65
ManyBooks   66
Mathematics: Introduction to Real Analysis   149
MERLOT: Multimedia Educational Resource for Learning and Online
        Teaching   67
Million Books Project *see* Digital Library of India
Missouri Botanic Gardens Rare Books   68
Mobile Learning: Transforming the Delivery of Education
        and Training   150
MobileRead   69
Mobipocket Free e-Books   70
Mortal Ghost   170, 220
Multimedia Educational Resource for Learning and Online Teaching   67
Munsey's Blackmask   71
National Defence University (Institute for National Strategic Studies) 118
New Georgia Encyclopedia   151
New York Botanical Garden, The LuEsther T. Mertz Library
        Rare Book Digitization Project   72
OER Commons   198
Ohio State University Press   119
Online Book Page   197
Open Access Textbooks Project   73
Open Book Project   74
Open Educational Resources (OER) Commons   198
Open Library   75
Open Textbooks   199

Orange Grove Open Textbooks 76
Oriental Institute of the University of Chicago 77
OverDrive Digital Media Locator 207
Oxford Text Archive 78
Page by Page Books 79
Palimpsest online 80
PDFse Ebook Search 208
Penn State Romance Studies 120
Perseus Digital Library (*also known as* The Perseus Hopper) 81
Planet eBook 82
Planet PDF: Free PDF eBooks Archive 226
Planned Obsolescence 171
PoemHunter.com: Free Poetry eBooks 83
Potto 84
Project Euclid 121
Project Gutenberg 85
Project Gutenberg of Australia 86
Project Gutenberg of Canada 86
Project Gutenberg of Germany 86
Project Runeberg 87
Public Literature 88
Read Classic Books Online 90
Reading About the World, Volume 1 152
ReadPrint 89
refdesk.com 200
Rice University Press 29
Roehampton University Children's Literature Collection 91
    See also Froebel Archive Digital Collection
Rotunda *see* University of Virginia Press
Royal College of Pathologists 127
Royal College of Surgeons of England 128
Runeberg Project 87
Shakespeare Quartos Archive 92
Shakespeare Quartos Archive *See also:* Works of the Bard.
    See also: William Shakespeare, The Complete Works of
    See also: William Shakespeare's Library
Shareware eBook.com 93
Shearsman Books 110
Smashwords 133
Smithsonian Institution Digital Library 94
Spartacus: Encyclopedia of the First World War 153, 221
Spineless Books 95
Stories from the Web 222
Temeraire Wiki: Victory of Eagles 173
Tennessee Encyclopedia of History and Culture 154
Textbook Media 96
Textbook Revolution 201
The Basement Interviews 161

The Platform Book 172
This Gaming Life: Travels in Three Cities 135
Tor.com 111
Turning the Pages™ 19
Under the Table 158
Universal Digital Library 97
Universal Library 98
University of Arizona Press 122
University of California 117
University of California Press eScholarship Editions Public Titles 123
University of North Carolina Greensboro English Department 116
University of Pittsburgh Press Digital Editions 124
University of Pretoria UPSpace: Special Collections – Africana 225
University of Virginia Electronic Texts Centre 99
University of Virginia Press 125
Victorian Prose Archive 100
Volramos 112
WattPad 134
We Tell Stories 159
We Think 175
Wealth of Networks 174
Wesleyan University Press 126
Wikibooks 101
Wikijunior 223
Wikipedia 176
        See also: Citizendium
William Shakespeare, The Complete Works of 102
        See also: Shakespeare Quartos Archive.
        See also: William Shakespeare's Library
        See also: Works of the Bard
William Shakespeare's Library 103
        See also: Complete Works of William Shakespeare
        See also: Shakespeare Quartos Archive.
        See also: Works of the Bard
Without Gods: Towards a History of Disbelief 177
        See also: Holy of Holies: On the Constituents of Emptiness
Works of the Bard 104
        See also: Complete Works of William Shakespeare
        See also: Shakespeare Quartos Archive.
        See also: William Shakespeare's Library
World eBook Library see World Public Library
World Public Library 105
WOWIO 106
Yale University School of Medicine Heart Book 155
Yale: Harvey Cushing/John Hay Whitney Medical Historical Library 107